Complete EnglishSmart

Grade **8**

Copyright © 2015 **Popular Book Company (Canada) Limited**

Printed in China

ISBN: 978-1-897164-42-6

Complete EnglishSmart Contents

ISBN: 978-1-897164-42-6

ISBN: 978-1-897164-42-6

ISBN: 978-1-897164-42-6

Section 1

Integrated Practice

ISBN: 978-1-897164-42-6

A Cross-Canada
Culinary Tour

Canada is a large country, with many distinct regions based on geography, political boundaries, and people's ethnic make-up. Naturally, this diversity has an important effect when it comes to food! While it may be easy for us to think of a national dish for Scotland (haggis), Japan (sushi), or Italy (spaghetti), it is difficult to imagine a food that exemplifies Canada. Instead, what we find, when we go from coast to coast, is a wide and delicious assortment of regional specialties. So, let's take a cross-Canada culinary tour.

If you were partaking of a home-style meal in Newfoundland, you would certainly find yourself tucking into baked codfish and blueberry pie. If you find yourself eating a lobster supper in a church basement, you could be in Nova Scotia or Prince Edward Island. Fiddlehead soup? These funny greens may have been picked in New Brunswick. If your baked bean casserole tastes a little sweet, with a hint of maple, then you're in Quebec. And if someone hands you a carton of French fries covered in brown gravy and melted cheese, don't back away! This French-Canadian dish is called poutine – and is very popular in Ottawa and the region.

If someone offers you a perogy, take it! You are now in western Canada – and you could very well be in the province of Manitoba, whose large Polish and Ukrainian populations introduced this food to our country more than a hundred years ago. Perogies are just mashed potato and cheese stuffed inside a pocket of dough, but don't let the simple ingredients fool you into thinking the dish is boring. Perogies are boiled, pan-fried, or deep fried, and usually eaten with sour cream, butter, and onions. Comfort food at its yummiest!

ISBN: 978-1-897164-42-6

If barbecued steak and buffalo burgers are on the menu, then welcome to Alberta, Canada's "cattle country". But, whoa...back up, pardner. If bannock appears on your bread plate and Saskatoon-berry pie is for dessert, then you may be in Saskatchewan – and what a mouthful of a word that is!

After all your dining adventures, you may be feeling a little bit full – but there's more! Head to Vancouver, British Columbia for the best Chinese and South Asian food in Canada. You can sip jasmine tea and eat dim sum in the hustle-bustle of Chinatown, or try an assortment of Thai spring rolls or Vietnamese rice-paper wraps at Granville Island Market...unless, of course, you want to try the catch of the day, fresh salmon...

Canada is an immigrant nation. The truth is, it wouldn't be too hard to find a world of cuisine in any large Canadian city. So dig in!

A. Write the food that best represents each of the following places in Canada.

Place	Food
Alberta	
Manitoba	
New Brunswick	
Newfoundland	
Nova Scotia	
Saskatchewan	
Quebec	
Vancouver	
Ottawa	

ISBN: 978-1-897164-42-6

B. Read the clues and complete the crossword puzzle with words from the passage.

Across

A.   thin cornbread baked in a griddle

B.   consuming heartily

C.   having a share of

D.   another word for partner

E.   products of particular superiority

Down

1.   serves as an example

2.   being different

3.   relating to cooking

4.   style of cooking that is characteristic of a place

ISBN: 978-1-897164-42-6

C. Based on the information given below, write about poutine and perogy.

- *name likely an adaptation of the English word "pudding"*
- *originated in rural Quebec in late 1950s*
- *consisting of French fries topped with fresh cheese curds and covered with hot gravy and sometimes other additional ingredients*
- *fresh cheese curds soft in the warm fries, without completely melting*
- *variation: Italian poutine, substitutes gravy with "spaghetti sauce"*

_____

_____

_____

_____

_____

_____

- *crescent-shaped dumplings*
- *stuffed with cheese, mashed potatoes, cabbage, onion, meat, or with a fruit filling*
- *fried or boiled until they float*
- *then covered with butter or oil*
- *served with plenty of sour cream*
- *topped with fried bacon or onions*
- *a 7.6-metre perogy, complete with fork , unveiled in the village of Glendon, Alberta in 1993*

_____

_____

_____

_____

_____

ISBN: 978-1-897164-42-6

Surprising Stories about
Sound

While you are enjoying your favourite music on your personal audio player, have you ever wondered about the mechanics of hearing? In order to understand how we hear, we must understand the dynamics of sounds and the features of the human ear.

Sound is a series of vibrations, and our ears work to decode these vibrations for us. First, the part of the ear we can see – the pinna (also called auricle) – collects these sound vibrations in the air. These vibrations travel down the ear canal to the eardrum. The eardrum vibrates. Next, there are three "ear bones" (also called ossicles) called the hammer, anvil, and stirrup. These tiny bones serve to magnify the vibrations of the eardrum. The vibrations move to the cochlea. The sensory cells inside this mechanism detect the vibrations and change them into messages. Finally, the messages are sent along the auditory nerve to the brain, giving us the sounds we want – or don't want – to hear.

For most of us, our sense of hearing works like a charm. But, compared to animals, humans cannot hear very well at all. Elephants, for example, often communicate at sound levels as low as five hertz. This means that if you flap your hands back and forth faster than five times a second, an elephant can actually hear the tone produced!

The behaviour of animals before earthquakes and other natural disasters gives us an indication of their superior hearing. For example, a deadly tsunami, caused by an earthquake on the ocean floor, hit the coastlines of several countries around the Indian Ocean in 2004, causing death to over 200 000 people. Surprisingly, most animals in national parks or zoos were reported to be unharmed.

In Thailand, the elephants that were being used to carry tourists escaped, if they were able, to higher ground long before the tsunami struck. The elephants were able to sense the vibration of the earthquakes through their feet, and they reacted instinctively by heading uphill. Moreover,

ISBN: 978-1-897164-42-6

the animals – even birds sitting in trees – were able to detect the vibrations from the incoming tsunami as well. Vibration from the tsunami is actually low frequency sound.

The frequency of a sound refers to the number of vibrations per second. The human ear can hear sounds with a frequency between 20 and 20 000 hertz. As we age, we gradually lose the ability to hear high frequency sounds. With this in mind, a clever inventor developed a tone with a frequency of 17 000 hertz. This tone, called the "Mosquito", has been utilized by convenience store owners to disperse young people lingering in front while leaving adult customers unaffected. This new technology was recently given the dubious distinction of an "Ig Nobel Award" (a spoof of the Nobel Prizes).

A. Write in your own words the main idea of each paragraph.

Paragraph	Main Idea
1	
2	
3	
4	
5	
6	

The "Mosquito" has been utilized by convenience store owners to disperse young people lingering in front while leaving adult customers unaffected. Do you think this is an acceptable way? Why or why not?

_____

_____

_____

_____

_____

ISBN: 978-1-897164-42-6

Sequencing

Things happen in order of events or sequence. Signal words like "first", "second", "next", "finally", "after", or "then" can identify the next event.

Example:

Topic Sentence → Sound is a series of vibrations, and our ears work to decode these vibrations for us. First, the pinna (also called auricle) collects these sound vibrations in the air. These vibrations travel down the ear canal to the eardrum. The eardrum vibrates. Next, there are three "ear bones" (also called ossicles) called the hammer, anvil, and stirrup. These tiny bones serve to magnify the vibrations of the eardrum. The vibrations move to the cochlea. The sensory cells inside this mechanism detect the vibrations and change them into messages. Finally, the messages are sent along the auditory nerve to the brain, giving us the sounds we want – or don't want – to hear.

Word to show sequencing ←

Word to show sequencing ←

Word to show sequencing ←

B. Sequence the sentences to form a cohesive paragraph. Write the letters.

A. The warm-up usually took at least ten minutes.

B. The first thing he did was to stretch his muscles to make sure that his muscles were ready.

C. He would take part in an individual race and a relay.

D. After running up the stadium steps, Don would do ten laps around the track.

E. Finally, he would run all the way home – a distance of about two kilometres.

F. Then, he would run up and down the flight of stairs in the stadium a couple of times before practising on the track.

G. To stay in top form, he practised each day after school at a nearby stadium.

H. Don was training intensively for the annual athletic meet.

1 → 2 → 3 → 4 → 5 → 6 → 7 → 8

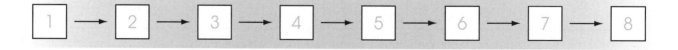 ISBN: 978-1-897164-42-6

Homograph

Homograph refers to words spelled in the same way but of different meanings or origins as well as words of identical spelling but different pronunciation.

Examples: *sound (noun) – what we hear*   *sound (adjective) – good, reliable*

lead (noun) – a metal   *lead (verb) – stay ahead*

C. Use each of the following words in sentences of your own to show different meanings.

1. sound

    a. _____

    b. _____

2. bear

    a. _____

    b. _____

3. well

    a. _____

    b. _____

4. ground

    a. _____

    b. _____

5. found

    a. _____

    b. _____

6. tie

    a. _____

    b. _____

ISBN: 978-1-897164-42-6

3

If – a Poem by Rudyard Kipling

Rudyard Kipling is famous as the author of *The Jungle Book* and *Kim*. But he was also a poet. Although this poem was written decades ago, it is still full of wisdom, for boys and girls alike.

If you can keep your head when all about you
Are losing theirs and blaming it on you;
If you can trust yourself when all men doubt you,
But make allowance for their doubting too;
If you can wait and not be tired by waiting,
Or being lied about, don't deal in lies,
Or being hated, don't give way to hating,
And yet don't look too good, nor talk too wise;

If you can dream – and not make dreams your master;
If you can think – and not make thoughts your aim;
If you can meet with Triumph and Disaster
And treat those two impostors just the same;
If you can bear to hear the truth you've spoken
Twisted by knaves to make a trap for fools,
Or watch the things you gave your life to, broken,
And stoop and build 'em up with worn-out tools;

A. Choose and underline the most appropriate answer.

1. *"If you can trust yourself when all men doubt you,
   But make allowance for their doubting too"*

   This is about _____ .

   A. self-confidence
   B. mutual trust
   C. self-doubt

2. *"If you can dream – and not make dreams your master"*

   This is about _____ .

   A. the ability to think big
   B. acting on your dream without being controlled by it
   C. being the master of your dreams

ISBN: 978-1-897164-42-6

If you can make one heap of all your winnings
And risk it on one turn of pitch-and-toss,
And lose, and start again at your beginnings,
And never breathe a word about your loss;
If you can force your heart and nerve and sinew
To serve your turn long after they are gone,
And so hold on when there is nothing in you
Except the Will which says to them: "Hold on!"

If you can talk with crowds and keep your virtue,
Or walk with kings – nor lose the common touch;
If neither foes nor loving friends can hurt you;
If all men count with you, but none too much;
If you can fill the unforgiving minute
With sixty seconds' worth of distance run,
Yours is the Earth and everything that's in it,
And – which is more – you'll be a Man, my son!

3. *"If you can make one heap of all your winnings*
   And risk it on one turn of pitch-and-toss,
   And lose, and start again at your beginnings,
   And never breathe a word about your loss"

   This is about _____ .

   A. the courage to take risks
   B. the joy of winning and the agony of losing
   C. how to start anew after losing

4. This poem is about _____ .

   A. how to develop the proper attitude towards life
   B. how to stay ahead of others
   C. how to play fair and be respected

ISBN: 978-1-897164-42-6

Which part of the poem impresses you most? Write it on the lines below and explain why this is so.

_____

_____

_____

_____

B. Read the clues and complete the crossword puzzle with words from Rudyard Kipling's "If".

Across

A. bend forward and downward

B. goodness

C. a cord joining a muscle to a bone

D. people who pose as others

E. dishonest people

Down

1. victory

2. extremely bad situation or accident

3. enemies

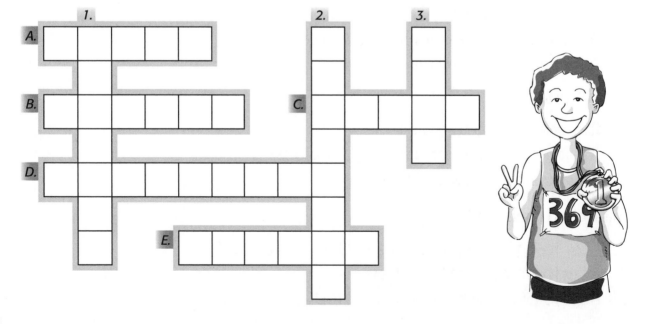

ISBN: 978-1-897164-42-6

Conditional Clauses

A **conditional clause** usually begins with "if" and it sets a condition under which something can be done.

Example: *You should have no problem passing the examination on condition that you spend more time reviewing the handouts.*

If you spend more time reviewing the handouts, you should have no problem passing the examination.

C. The following are taken from the poem "If". Complete the sentences with ideas of your own.

1. If you can trust yourself when all men doubt you,

   _____

   _____

2. If you can wait and not be tired by waiting,

   _____

   _____

3. If you can think – and not make thoughts your aim,

   _____

   _____

4. If neither foes nor loving friends can hurt you,

   _____

   _____

5. If you can make one heap of all your winnings, and risk it on one turn of pitch-and-toss, and lose, and start again at your beginnings, and never breathe a word about your loss,

   _____

   _____

ISBN: 978-1-897164-42-6

correspondent (n)
= journalist
= reporter

Books Change Lives

plight (n) 困境苦境
publication.
anonymous 匿名.無名
royalty.

Books change lives – not just for those who learn to read and are <u>inspired</u> by the stories, but sometimes for the subject of the books, if the book <u>is based on</u> a true story. This is exactly what happened to a young Chinese girl named Ma Yan, who lived an <u>anonymous</u> life in a <u>remote village</u> called Zhang Jia Shu in Ningxia province in China just a few years ago. Today, Ma Yan is known around the world.

When Ma Yan was 13 years old, she wrote in her diary about her worries that she would not be able to continue her education because her parents could not afford to keep her in school. In May of 2001, a group of foreigners and journalists visited her boarding school, and someone gave Ma Yan's diary to the visitors to read. Pierre Haski, a Beijing <u>correspondent</u> for the French publication *Libération*, read it and wanted to help. He gave the Ma family a small gift of money and wrote about their <u>plight</u> in his <u>publication</u> in early 2002. Suddenly, people began to send money. The story was so popular that Ma Yan's diary was translated into French and published in France. It soon sold over 50 000 copies, and was quickly translated into Italian, Swedish, Dutch, Japanese, Greek, Spanish, and Portuguese.

<u>By the time</u> it was translated into English and published, the title needed to be changed! It had originally been titled *Ma Yan's Diary – The Daily Life of a Chinese Schoolgirl*, but <u>because of</u> the success of the French publication, Ma Yan and her family now had enough money for her schooling and other necessities. Ma Yan and Haski had given 25% of their <u>royalties</u> of the French publication to the Association for the Children of Ningxia, <u>set up</u> to

royalty 版税

ISBN: 978-1-897164-42-6

assist the children of Ma Yan's home province. The English version of the book has been called *The Diary of Ma Yan: The Life of a Chinese Schoolgirl – Transformed*, which shows us that the power of the written word can indeed change lives!

Ma Yan's story is being adapted into a movie. It will show the life of a young girl from a poor family who wants an education, but finds it difficult to break away from the destiny of so many of China's women today: leaving school early to help on the farms. Thanks to the success of Ma Yan's story, the destiny of many of the girls from Ma Yan's home area will get the education they dream of.

[handwritten annotations: fate; be adapted into; break away : get rid of 摆脱]

A. Answer these questions.

1. How does the success of Ma Yan's story benefit other children in Ma Yan's home province?

   [handwritten answer: They will get the education they dream of.]

2. Do you agree that the new title "*The Diary of Ma Yan: The Life of a Chinese Schoolgirl – Transformed*" is more powerful and relevant than the original one? Why or why not?

3. What do you think accounts for the popularity of Ma Yan's diary around the world?

   [handwritten annotation: (n) 声望]

4. The writer uses the title "*Books Change Lives*" to highlight how Ma Yan and others' lives have been changed as a result of the publishing of her diary. Is there another way that books can change our lives?

ISBN: 978-1-897164-42-6

This is an entry in Ma Yan's journal: *"I couldn't really walk any farther, but Mother forced us to go (and haul bales of buckwheat). Well, how could I refuse her? She exhausts herself to provide food for us when there's nothing left, and then she exhausts herself all over again, without getting anything out of life for herself. She doesn't want us to live the way she does. That's why we have to study. We'll be happy. Unlike her."* From the entry, can you tell what Ma Yan's mother was hoping for, and what Ma Yan's aspirations were?

_____

_____

_____

_____

_____

_____

_____

B. Give a derivative of each of the following words. Write the derivative in a sentence of your own to illustrate its meaning.

1. inspired – _____

_____

2. popular – _____

_____

3. necessities – _____

_____

4. transformed – _____

_____

ISBN: 978-1-897164-42-6

C. **Imagine you are Pierre Haski. Tell your audience about your encounter with the 13-year-old Ma Yan in Zhang Jia Shu and what prompted you to help Ma Yan publish her diary.**

ISBN: 978-1-897164-42-6

5

Saint-Pierre and *Miquelon*

Did you know there's a little piece of Europe right next to Canada? No, this is not a reference to Quebec, although the old buildings and cobblestone streets of places like Québec City do look very European. There are several small islands off the coast of Newfoundland where people sing "La Marseillaise" instead of "Oh Canada", speak a kind of French that is not spoken in Quebec – and pay in Euros.

This unique territory is called Saint-Pierre and Miquelon, and it also includes the smaller islands of Grand Colombier, Petit Colombier, and Île aux Marins. The total area of the territory is about 250 square kilometres, with a coastline of about 120 km. Although it is small, and has only about 6500 residents, the tiny French territory has a fascinating history, and is still very much "on the map" so to speak, at least in Canada and France.

Saint-Pierre and Miquelon has belonged to France, on and off, since 1763, when parts of Canada were the colony of New France. But its history of European settlement goes back further than that. It was an important stop on the cod fishery as far back as the 16th century, when French and Basque fishermen went there to fish the plentiful waters of the Grand Banks off the coast of Newfoundland. In the early 20th century, during Prohibition (when the United States Government declared illegal the manufacturing and selling of liquor), Saint Pierre and Miquelon was used as a base for smuggling alcoholic beverages, produced in both Canada and France, into the United States.

Today, the existence of these French islands means that French fishermen have access to fishing areas that the Canadian government felt should be shared. An international court ruled in 1992 that France was entitled to an exclusive fishing zone of around 24 nautical miles around Saint-Pierre and Miquelon. Boundary disputes between Canada and France flare up from time to time.

As the cod-fishing industry becomes more unstable, the government of France is trying to diversify the economy of Saint-Pierre and Miquelon, by developing the tourism, fish farming, and crab-fishing industries. Saint-Pierre and

22

Miquelon

Saint-Pierre

ISBN: 978-1-897164-42-6

Miquelon has two airports, so you can fly there from Newfoundland, Nova Scotia, New Brunswick, and Montreal, Quebec. There is a regular ferry service between Saint-Pierre and the town of Fortune, Newfoundland. The climate is considered bleak throughout much of the year; it is often damp and windy, with long, hard winters. Late summer and early fall are the best times to visit. And why not visit? In the age when everyone seems to have been everywhere, a tourist coming back with stories of Saint-Pierre and Miquelon would stand out in a crowd.

A. Check the main idea of each paragraph.

Paragraph One

_____ A. There are a few small islands off Newfoundland that belong to France.

_____ B. The Euro is used on several small islands off Newfoundland.

Paragraph Two

_____ A. Saint-Pierre and Miquelon is about 250 square kilometres, with a coastline of about 120 km.

_____ B. Although Saint-Pierre and Miquelon is small, we can find it on the map.

Paragraph Three

_____ A. Saint-Pierre and Miquelon has belonged to France, on and off, since 1763, when parts of Canada were the colony of New France.

_____ B. Saint-Pierre and Miquelon was an important stop on the cod fishery as far back as the 16th century and a base for smuggling alcoholic beverages into the United States in the early 20th century.

Paragraph Four

_____ A. Today, French fishermen have access to the fishing areas around Saint-Pierre and Miquelon that the Canadian government thinks should be shared.

_____ B. Canada and France are often involved in disputes over Saint-Pierre and Miquelon.

Paragraph Five

_____ A. France is trying to develop tourism, fish farming, and crab-fishing on Saint-Pierre and Miquelon.

_____ B. Saint-Pierre and Miquelon is easily accessible from Newfoundland, Nova Scotia, New Brunswick, and Montreal, Quebec.

ISBN: 978-1-897164-42-6

Paraphrasing

A **paraphrase** is your own rendition of someone else's ideas, expressed in a new form.

Example: *This unique territory is called Saint-Pierre and Miquelon, and it also includes the smaller islands of Grand Colombier, Petit Colombier, and Île aux Marins. (original)*

Saint-Pierre and Miquelon is a unique territory that includes the smaller islands of Grand Colombier, Petit Colombier, and Île aux Marins. (paraphrase)

B. Paraphrase the following statements taken from the passage.

1. The tiny French territory has a fascinating history, and is still very much "on the map" so to speak, at least in Canada and France.

    _____

    _____

    _____

2. Boundary disputes between Canada and France flare up from time to time.

    _____

    _____

    _____

3. Today, the existence of these French islands means that French fishermen have access to fishing areas that the Canadian government felt should be shared.

    _____

    _____

    _____

4. In the age when everyone seems to have been everywhere, a tourist coming back with stories of Saint-Pierre and Miquelon would stand out in a crowd.

    _____

    _____

    _____

ISBN: 978-1-897164-42-6

C. **Based on the passage, write a short article about Saint-Pierre and Miquelon that provides useful information for those who contemplate visiting this French territory. Your writing is meant to inform as well as arouse their interest.**

Welcome to Saint-Pierre and Miquelon, where

France meets North America! _____

_____

_____

_____

_____

_____

_____

_____

_____

_____

_____

_____

_____

_____

_____

_____

_____

_____

_____

_____

ISBN: 978-1-897164-42-6

Dealing with Stress in Japan

Studies have shown that stress can have an adverse effect on our bodies. Initially, when we are first stressed by something (such as a loud noise), our bodies respond by creating adrenaline and other neuropeptides. Our blood pressure rises, as does our body temperature, our heart rate, and our oxygen consumption. We are ready to give "fight or flight" so to speak, as our caveman ancestors would have done if they came across a sabre-toothed tiger.

But if we are dealing with stress over a long period of time – for example, in the workplace – the effect on our bodies is not healthy. Toxins accumulate from the "fight or flight" response, causing cells in our bodies to age or die prematurely. After long-term stress exposure, our reaction times decrease, our mental functions start to slip, and we may suffer from insomnia, depression, or angry outbursts. Over time, people can die from stress.

The first reported case of karoshi (death from overwork) in Japan occurred in 1969 with the death from a stroke of a 29-year-old married male worker in the shipping department of Japan's largest newspaper company. In 1987, the Ministry of Labour started publishing statistics on this new epidemic. In 2004, there were 345 karoshi-related deaths in Japan, an increase over the previous year. Moreover, lack of sleep is deemed the cause for 40% of work-related accidents and absenteeism there.

Meditation and relaxation are good ways to help reduce the effects of stress, but how does one go about getting the needed peace and quiet in a busy city? Recently, some enterprising people in Japan have started providing products and services to help stressed-out Japanese workers cope. Sales of "desk pillows" are booming, and nap salons are opening in the country's urban centres.

ISBN: 978-1-897164-42-6

These nap salons, with names such as Hotel Siesta, Business Inn Pillow, and Good Sleep Salon Napia, offer a bed for sleep sessions from 15 minutes to two hours, with the price ranging from $5 to $16. Some establishments offer a cup of coffee to drink before lying down, as the caffeine takes about 20 minutes to take effect, the optimal amount of time for a workday catnap, according to Japan's Ministry of Education, Culture, Sports, Science and Technology. Japan's Sleep Research Institute has designed a talking pillow with sensors that learn the user's regular sleep habits. Depending on head movements, the pillow is programmed to offer 40 messages, including advice like "Try taking a warm bath" and positive reinforcement like "You've been sleeping great. Keep it up."

A. Write the main point of each paragraph in the chart below.

Paragraph	Main Point
1	
2	
3	
4	
5	

What is the most common cause for your stress? How would you deal with stress?

_____

_____

_____

_____

ISBN: 978-1-897164-42-6

B. The paragraph below shows how the sentences relate to one another. In a similar way, develop a paragraph from each of the following two topic sentences.

Topic Sentence ⟶ But if we are dealing with stress over a long period of time – for example, in the workplace – the effect on our bodies is not healthy. Toxins accumulate from the "fight or flight" response, causing cells in our bodies to age or die prematurely. ⟵ Explaining why it is not healthy

After long-term stress exposure, our reaction times decrease, our Further elaboration ⟶ mental functions start to slip, and we may suffer from insomnia, depression, or angry outbursts. Over time, people can die from stress. ⟵ Worst case scenario

1. Nap salons in Japan are offering more and more services. _____

_____

_____

_____

_____

_____

_____

2. Exercise is a good way to de-stress. _____

_____

_____

_____

_____

_____

_____

ISBN: 978-1-897164-42-6

Inversion

Inversion adds style to your writing and makes it more interesting to read.

Examples: *Exercise helps us relieve stress. A quick nap helps us relieve stress, too.*
Exercise helps us relieve stress and so does a quick nap.
Exercise helps us relieve stress, as does a quick nap.

Sam doesn't help much. Janet doesn't help much, either.
Sam doesn't help much, and neither does Janet.

C. Join the following pairs of sentences using inversion.

1. Yoga has a calming and soothing effect. Meditation has that effect too.

   _____

   _____

   _____

2. You shouldn't work too late. You shouldn't skip dinner, either.

   _____

   _____

3. Mr. Watson doesn't know how to relax. His son doesn't know how to do so, either.

   _____

   _____

4. Patricia suffered from insomnia. Jason suffered from insomnia, too.

   _____

   _____

5. The workers took a quick nap after lunch. I took a quick nap after lunch too.

   _____

   _____

ISBN: 978-1-897164-42-6

Canadians & Americans:
What Makes Us Different?

People who have visited or lived in North America will often talk about certain differences between Canadians and Americans: Canadians are modest, reserved, and understated while their southern neighbours are more exuberant. As many generalizations go, this one is rooted in truth.

So, why are we different? Political events over hundreds of years have shaped our two countries differently. While both countries began as British colonies, the United States fought and won a war of independence from Britain back in 1776. So, while the United States became a republic, Canada remained part of the British Empire and developed into a constitutional monarchy. Even today, the Queen of England still reigns as the Queen of Canada.

Also, the settlement patterns of the two countries differ. In the United States, the west was being settled by various groups of people heading out on their own in search of free land and the "American dream". Towns sprung up in the American west, with little government control. In fact, the term "the Wild West" is related to the idea that the American frontier was a place where men and women could live independently. As the government stepped in to provide the lawful authority of the land, they oftentimes had difficulty dealing with this type of individualistic person of the American frontier.

By contrast, the Canadian west was settled under the auspices of the government to begin with. For the most part, the North West Mounted Police headed out in order to establish relations with the Aboriginal communities and traders before large-scale European settlement occurred. In this way, the Canadian population developed into a society that was more compliant, more respectful of authority, and less "individualistic". It is important not to underestimate the effect of this difference on our societies today. Canadian society is more

ISBN: 978-1-897164-42-6

communal in nature, not so readily espousing the "every man to himself" mentality that was needed to survive the American "Wild West".

When looking at history in this way, it is perhaps not surprising that Canadians value their free health care system, paid for communally through taxation, and that Canadians do not have the right to bear arms written into the country's constitution, which is the case in the United States. So...what kind of person do you think you most resemble? And where would you rather live?

A. Answer these questions.

1. Explain in your words: "Political events over hundreds of years have shaped our two countries differently."

_____

_____

2. How did the term "the Wild West" come up?

_____

_____

3. Why are Canadians generally more compliant, more respectful of authority, and less individualistic?

_____

_____

Do you think the differences between Canadians and Americans are easily noticeable? Give examples to support your view.

_____

_____

_____

_____

_____

ISBN: 978-1-897164-42-6

Transition Words and Phrases

Transition words and **phrases** help establish clear connections between ideas and ensure that sentences and paragraphs flow smoothly, making them easy to read.

Some common words and phrases to show similar ideas: also, moreover, likewise, in fact, by the same token, etc.

Some common words and phrases to show different ideas: on the other hand, however, by contrast, etc.

B. Use appropriate transition words or phrases to improve the flow of each pair of sentences below.

1. The Pythons have lost five games in a row. The Eagles seem invincible and are poised to win the division title.

   _____

   _____

2. More has to be done to rectify the situation. We may need outside help to speed things up.

   _____

   _____

3. He stands a good chance of getting the job. The intervention of the chairman may complicate things.

   _____

   _____

4. Don is always so helpful, amicable, and cheerful. His brother Jason appears to be ill-tempered, impatient, and grumpy.

   _____

   _____

5. Harrison does not show any sign of improvement whatsoever. He is getting more and more unreasonable.

   _____

   _____

ISBN: 978-1-897164-42-6

C. **While Canadians and Americans may have many differences, we do have something in common. Write a short article about our similarities, giving some everyday examples such as sports, entertainment, and customs.**

ISBN: 978-1-897164-42-6

The World of
Third Culture Kids

Emily was born in Beijing, spent two years in Yugoslavia (where her sister was born), and then three years in Kenya. At eight she moved to Hong Kong for seven years. Her mother is French, her father is Canadian, and her sister, who hasn't had as peripatetic a life, often wonders what her sister's concerns about identity are all about. Believe it or not, more and more children are living lives like this, as "global nomads" or "Third Culture Kids".

The term "Third Culture Kid" (shortened to TCK) was coined in the 1960s by Drs. Ruth and John Useem, who used it to define the experience of primarily immigrant children growing up between two cultures: their culture of "origin" (or that of their parents) and the place they were currently living. In today's global society, the TCK term also refers to children who have travelled a lot and who are "culturally blended": familiar with many cultures and not as familiar with the culture of the parents. It has been said that Third Culture Kids represent the single fastest growing population in the world today.

Parents assume that their own culture is their children's culture. But what if you are growing up in a different place from where your parents did? Psychologists studying the lives of mobile families say that it is quite common for parents to minimize their children's sense of confusion regarding where they fit in; they don't understand that their children have different ideas about what "home" is.

Any child would face anxieties when moving homes, even to a different neighbourhood. But these issues are compounded when a child is put into a different culture, and must deal with language issues and cultural differences, and finding themselves in a new place in society. But TCK experts agree that the advantages of being a "child of the world" outweigh the disadvantages, if the parents can help the children see the opportunity they've been given.

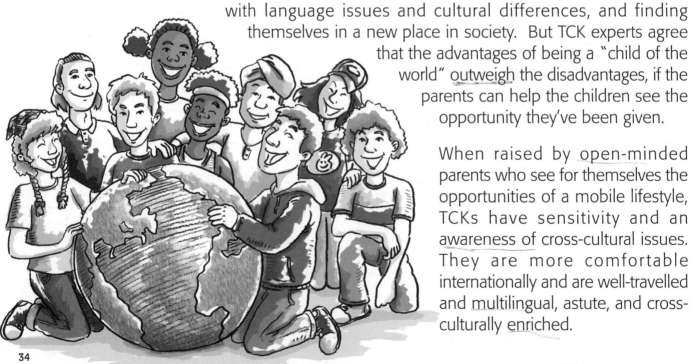

When raised by open-minded parents who see for themselves the opportunities of a mobile lifestyle, TCKs have sensitivity and an awareness of cross-cultural issues. They are more comfortable internationally and are well-travelled and multilingual, astute, and cross-culturally enriched.

ISBN: 978-1-897164-42-6

The majority of TCKs continue the transient lifestyle as adults. TCKs can be reminded that while they may not identify with any one culture, they are a part of the growing "culture" of people the world over, who feel at home in many places, and consider themselves a part of all of them.

A. Answer these questions.

1. Explain in your own words what Third Culture Kids are.

_____

_____

2. What do you think are the causes for more and more TCKs?

_____

_____

3. What are some common problems that TCKs have to face?

_____

_____

4. Why does the writer think that being a TCK has more advantages than disadvantages?

_____

_____

 **In what way can TCKs foster better understanding and acceptance among people of different cultures? If possible, cite an example to support your answer.**

_____

_____

_____

_____

_____

ISBN: 978-1-897164-42-6

Cohesive Writing

Cohesion is the glue that holds a piece of writing together. Cohesive devices include transitional words and phrases that clarify the relationships among ideas in a piece of writing.

B. Rearrange each of the following groups of sentences to form a cohesive paragraph.

Group 1

A. Keeping that in mind, children and adolescents often adjust quickly and easily to life overseas.

B. The family needs to plan carefully, set realistic expectations for all family members, and be ready to identify and handle problems as they happen.

C. The adjustment to life overseas is not without difficulties for young people.

_____   _____   _____

Group 2

A. In fact, international exposure at an early age appears to have an enduring impact that positively shapes both children and adults.

B. Many parents who want to pursue an international career assignment or educational opportunity may feel that they cannot or should not because moving abroad may be detrimental to their children.

C. However, research suggests that such fears are unfounded.

_____   _____   _____

Group 3

A. One of the most notable areas in which adult TCKs differ from their peers who have not lived abroad is their level of education.

B. Respondents credited their academic achievements to the high quality of overseas schools and to educated parents.

C. According to a study, people who spent at least one year of their childhood away from their home country were four times more likely to earn a bachelor's degree.

_____   _____   _____

ISBN: 978-1-897164-42-6

C. **Read the clues and complete the crossword puzzle with words from the passage.**

Across

A. created and used for the first time (about words)
B. travelling around a lot
C. traits of a person that distinguish him or her from others
D. lasting only a short time
E. mixed together
F. people who travel from place to place

Down

1. moving freely
2. have greater importance or benefit than the other
3. worries, nervousness
4. skilful at understanding behaviours or situations
5. take something as true
6. those who study the human mind

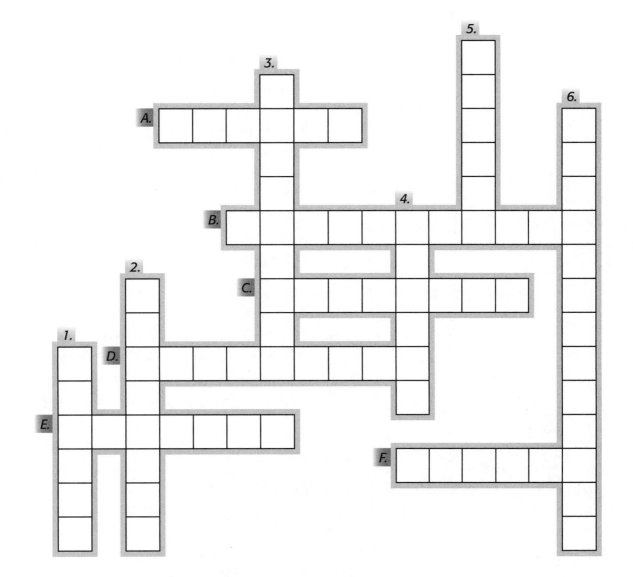

ISBN: 978-1-897164-42-6

Beppu, Japan
Making the Most of Living on the Fault Line

Traditional Japanese culture is renowned for its peaceful aesthetic. We can see it in the tea ceremony, we can hear it in the sound of the koto, we can even taste it in the mild flavours of sushi and soba. But to feel it, there is no better way than to head to what is one of Japan's most delightful experiences, the outdoor hot spring bath.

Because Japan is located atop shifting tectonic plates, it is used to frequent earthquakes and a lot of geothermal activity. Hot springs can be found from one end of the country to the other, but perhaps the place where the thermal dynamics are couched in the most spectacularly, serenely beautiful countryside is in the heart of the southern main island of Kyushu. Most well-known is the coastal city of Beppu, located in Oita Prefecture.

The word *onsen* means hot springs, and *rotemburo* refers to the outdoor hot spring bath. These can range from man-made pools outside hotel rooms to the most splendid natural pools surrounded by dense vegetation. A soak in an outdoor hot spring bath while the snow falls on you, with *yuzu* (large locally-grown citrus fruit) bobbing around, after a hike in the mountains, and followed by a hearty Japanese meal in front of an open hearth at a traditional inn, is an unforgettable delight.

Beppu, a resort city with a population of over 125 000, is considered the onsen capital of Japan. These hot springs are not only relaxing, but are claimed to have healing properties as well: a cure for everything from diabetes to psoriasis to arthritis. Beppu is located on Beppu Bay, and flanked along the back by Mt. Tsurumi and a ridge of hills. You can see steam rising in places throughout the city, giving it a netherworldly feel. The

ISBN: 978-1-897164-42-6

city's brochures boast that it has 2850 vents, making it the number one spot in Japan in terms of the number of sources and "gush volume".

Beppu is also known for its nine *jigoku* or "hells", which are hot springs (primarily tourist sites, not baths) of various sizes, colours, and mineral content, as well as bubbling mud pots and geysers surrounded by botanical gardens. The *umi-jigoku* (sea hell) is a bright cobalt blue, while the *chi-no-ike-jigoku* (blood pond hell) holds deep rust-coloured water. At Takegawara Spa, one can take a *suna-yu*, or sand bath, as well as a mud bath. If you are intrigued by geothermal energy, then you will certainly want to pay a visit to Japan – and the "steaming" resort city of Beppu.

A. Answer these questions.

1. What message do you think the writer intends to convey by including "*Making the Most of Living on the Fault Line*" in the title?

_____

_____

2. "...But to feel it, there is no better way than to head to what is one of Japan's most delightful experiences, the outdoor hot spring bath." What does "it" refer to?

_____

_____

3. Explain why hot springs abound in Japan.

_____

_____

4. What are "hells" in Beppu?

_____

_____

5. The writer feels that "a soak in an outdoor hot spring bath while the snow falls on you, with *yuzu* bobbing around, after a hike in the mountains, and followed by a hearty Japanese meal in front of an open hearth at a traditional inn, is an unforgettable delight." What is your ideal way to spend a day in Beppu?

_____

_____

ISBN: 978-1-897164-42-6

B. Read the clues and complete the crossword puzzle with words from the passage.

Across

A. moving up and down quickly

B. hot springs

C. relating to the internal heat of the Earth

D. restoring to health

E. the floor of a fireplace that extends into the room

F. substantial, abundant

Down

1. guarded

2. pleasure

3. famous

4. a place for holidaying

5. like the world of the dead

6. artistic beauty

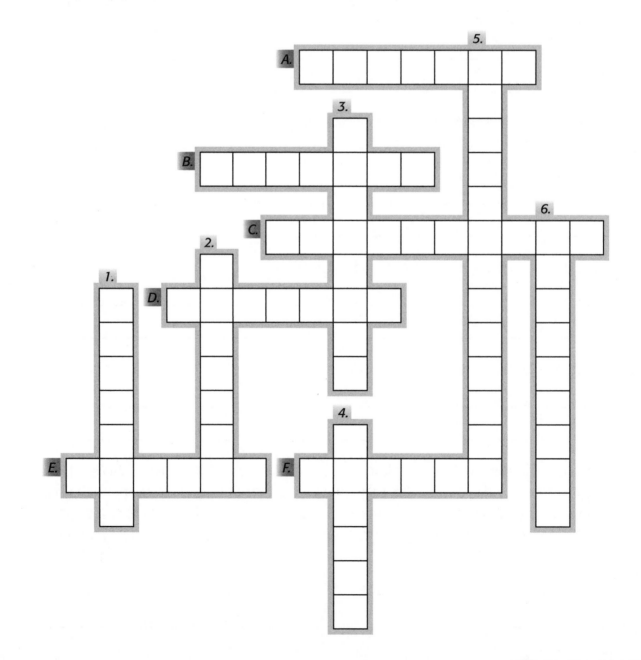

ISBN: 978-1-897164-42-6

C. **Combine each of the following groups of sentences by using conjunctions or turning some sentences into phrases or clauses.**

Example: *Japan is located atop shifting tectonic plates.*
It is used to frequent earthquakes.
There is a lot of geothermal activity in Japan.

Because Japan is located atop shifting tectonic plates, it is used to frequent earthquakes and a lot of geothermal activity.

1. A popular form of outdoor hot spring bath is the so-called waterfall. It comfortably massages your shoulders if you sit below it.

_____

_____

_____

2. *Ashiyu* are shallow hot spring pools for bathing just your feet. They are found in the streets of many hot spring resorts. They can be used free of charge.

_____

_____

_____

3. The hot springs in Japan are distinguished by the minerals dissolved in the water. Different minerals provide different health benefits. All hot springs are supposed to have a relaxing and soothing effect.

_____

_____

_____

4. When you enter a Japanese house, you should take off your shoes at the entrance. Then you should change into slippers. The slippers are usually provided by the host.

_____

_____

_____

ISBN: 978-1-897164-42-6

Music –
Our Most Reliable Therapy

Our cave-dwelling ancestors used it to get ready for the hunt, Egyptian priests made it an integral part of the mummification process – even Aristotle and Plato wrote about it. Whether it is used to soothe the beast in us, uplift us, or heal our bodies and minds, music has been our most reliable therapy since time began.

In more recent years, music and its therapeutic qualities became an important element in nursing homes, hospitals, and mental health centres. It was introduced after World War II as a community service when musicians were invited to perform at veteran's hospitals to help soldiers overcome the mental and physical traumas of combat. Since then, music as therapy has expanded in all directions; it now is called upon to work its magic on newborns – and even pre-borns. It has made the jump from humans to animals as well; just as moms-to-be will snatch up CDs of *Baby Loves Beethoven* off store shelves, the idea of calming your pet Persian with a bit of Mozart is no longer something to sneeze at.

In the burgeoning spa industry, the sound of music is being used to help us escape from an increasingly over-stimulating world. We are turning to music as a way to relax, refresh, and rejuvenate – even to go on a mental journey away from the everyday life. But there are some things to consider when choosing music to help you de-stress. Ideally the music should be relaxing but not too loud. Even soothing music at an incorrect level will prevent relaxation. And there is a danger in using pop music. Even if a pop song may have a tone and beat that is calming, it can also have mental connections to experiences in the listener's life that can make relaxation difficult. The words in songs can also act as a trigger to memories. For these reasons, music with lyrics should be avoided.

Sound has the ability to create an emotional and physical response. The sound of running water can actually relax the brain and body. But waterfalls, waves on the sand, and babbling brooks are not the only sounds of nature that can put our bodies and minds to rest. Some

ISBN: 978-1-897164-42-6

musicians and sound engineers have gone deep into the rainforest to offer us a listen to birds and even insects – as if we were sitting in the forest canopy. Echolocation – the sounds of dolphins and whales in communication – has also been sampled in this kind of "New Age" music. Next time you head to the music store to buy a new CD, why not treat yourself to a sampling of this new genre of music?

A. Identify the topic sentence in each of the paragraphs.

Paragraph 1 _____

Paragraph 2 _____

_____

Paragraph 3 _____

_____

Paragraph 4 _____

B. Answer these questions.

1. "...it (music) now is called upon to work its magic on newborns – and even pre-borns." What example does the writer give to illustrate her point?

   _____

   _____

2. Why does the writer think that pop songs may not help us relax and rejuvenate?

   _____

   _____

   _____

3. "Next time you head to the music store to buy a new CD, why not treat yourself to a sampling of this new genre of music." What is the new genre of music that the writer is referring to?

   _____

   _____

ISBN: 978-1-897164-42-6

Do you agree that music is our most reliable therapy? Why or why not?

_____

_____

_____

_____

_____

_____

C. Explain the following phrases in your own words.

1. an integral part

    _____

2. to soothe the beast in us

    _____

3. the mental and physical traumas of combat

    _____

4. something to sneeze at

    _____

5. the burgeoning spa industry

    _____

6. an increasingly over-stimulating world

    _____

7. a trigger to memories

    _____

ISBN: 978-1-897164-42-6

D. Develop each of the following topic sentences into a paragraph.

1. Nature is actually filled with the sound of music. _____

_____

_____

_____

_____

_____

2. Soothing music helps us unwind after a day's work. _____

_____

_____

_____

_____

_____

3. The proliferation of MP3 players is a good indication that music is a big part of our lives.

_____

_____

_____

_____

_____

_____

_____

ISBN: 978-1-897164-42-6

Rafflesia –
a True Floral Wonder

Everyone loves flowers. From the tiniest sprig of honeysuckle that heralds spring with its familiar scent, to huge, dripping bouquets of tropical blooms that can fill a room with heady fragrance, there is a flower to suit every preference. But there is one flower that is not likely to please anyone – and what a pity, too, as it is the largest flower in the world!

The Rafflesia, named after Sir Thomas Stamford Raffles, British explorer and administrator, and founder of the city of Singapore, was "discovered" – or rather, documented in English for the first time – in 1818, in the rainforest of Indonesia during a research excursion by British naturalist Dr. Joseph Arnold.

The most striking thing about the Rafflesia, and its more than 15 different species, is not its size, however. It is the putrid smell! A Rafflesia in bloom gives off an odour akin to rotting meat or even human decomposition. It is not surprising that the name for these flowers in local languages translates as "meat flower" or "corpse flower". It is believed that the smell serves an important purpose, however: to attract the flower's pollinators, such as flies and beetles.

The Rafflesia is a parasitic plant; it depends on another plant to thrive and grow. The Rafflesia has no stem and no leaves, and no root, which makes it necessary for the flowering plant to adhere itself onto another plant, the Tetrastigma vine. The vine has special fungus-like tissue that provides nutrients to the Rafflesia, enabling it to grow to its enormous size. The five petals of its bloom, mostly an orange colour with spots, can grow to a size of 106 centimetres and weigh almost 10 kilograms.

ISBN: 978-1-897164-42-6

Despite its size and strength, the Rafflesia's life is short-lived. It takes about a year for the flower to grow to full size, at which point it will start to bloom. The flower stays in bloom for a week before dying. Despite the odour, nature enthusiasts, as well as tourists, come to the rainforests of Southeast Asia to see the Rafflesia in bloom, and to smell the famous odour for themselves.

So famous is the flower that when a Rafflesia growing in the botanical garden of any city throughout the world begins to bloom, the event is likely to merit a word or two on the local evening news. The Rafflesia is an official state flower of Sabah province, in Malaysian Borneo, and also Surat Thani province, in Thailand.

A. Explain in your own words the following phrases as used in the passage.

1. floral wonder

   _____

2. the tiniest sprig of honeysuckle

   _____

3. heralds spring

   _____

4. heady fragrance

   _____

5. the most striking

   _____

6. the putrid smell

   _____

7. akin to

   _____

8. a parasitic plant

   _____

9. nature enthusiasts

   _____

10. to merit a word or two on the local evening news

    _____

ISBN: 978-1-897164-42-6

Summarizing

Summarizing is how we reduce a text to its bare essentials: the gist, the key ideas, and the main points that are worth noting and remembering.

In summarizing, we:

- pull out main ideas
- focus on key details
- use key words and phrases
- break down the larger ideas
- leave out examples and illustrations
- write only enough to convey the gist

B. Summarize each of the following paragraphs, using as few words as possible.

1. We need air to breathe, water to drink, and food to eat, but there is a growing number of people on Earth so we have to share everything with more and more people. The growing number of cars also causes severe air pollution. Factories produce a large amount of carbon dioxide, lead poisons, etc. which get into the air, too. Some of them in combination with water make sulfuric acid in the clouds, which later falls as acid rain that kills trees and make soil infertile.

_____

_____

_____

2. An estimated 220 pandas live in the Qinling Mountains, situated in China's central Shaanxi province. Once found across China, Myanmar, and Vietnam, fewer than 1000 pandas are now thought to remain in just six mountain ranges in southwest China. Within the Qinling Mountains, habitat fragmentation is the pressing threat. Some protected habitat patches are so divided by settlements, roads, and agricultural land that pandas find it impossible to move between reserves. The forests are slowly getting "nibbled up" by development.

_____

_____

_____

ISBN: 978-1-897164-42-6

C. **In no more than 100 words, write a summary of "Rafflesia – a True Floral Wonder". Include only the essentials.**

ISBN: 978-1-897164-42-6

Ethics in Science:
Cloning and
Genetic
Modification

Advances in technology have reached levels that we could not have believed possible only generations ago. Some of the things we now know are possible existed only in science fiction books. But now, technology is creating ethical dilemmas for us that are difficult to agree on. Two such examples are cloning and genetic modification of foods.

Cloning is not science fiction – it has been done. In 1997, Dolly, a sheep, was cloned by British scientists. Soon after, an Italian doctor said he and his team of geneticists would attempt to clone a human being someday. He said that human cloning would bring the hope of producing children to infertile couples, and would put an end to many diseases. Others say that the cloning of humans can result in the creation of unhealthy and malformed children and genetic monsters.

Some countries have banned all forms of cloning, but others allow it for scientific purposes such as stem cell research. Many scientists say that this type of therapeutic cloning (harnessing stem cells from cloned embryos) is ethical because health care branches can and do benefit from genetic studies. So, from science and biomedical conferences around the world, we see photos in the newspapers of advances in genetic engineering: a rat and rabbit with human ears jutting from their bodies, and cloned animals.

We also know of other "advances": fast-growing fish swimming in tanks, pest-resistant wheat, and some perfectly round, red tomatoes – all genetically modified. Genetically modified (GM) foods containing genes derived from bacteria and viruses as well as foods with insect, fish, and animal genes are now widely used. Some 32 000 items in U.S. grocery stores already contain GM organisms. These include tomatoes, corn, potatoes, and soybeans.

ISBN: 978-1-897164-42-6

Although there are benefits, there are concerns; the cross-species transfers that result do not happen in nature and may create new toxins or other risks. Transferring animal genes into plants also raises important ethical issues for individuals, vegetarians, and religious groups, who have the right to know what exactly they are eating – and say they do not want fish, insects, or eventually humans in their tomatoes or corn! Moreover, the resulting new "species" may change the balance of nature in a given ecosystem by creating "super species" resistant to herbicides and pests. Anti-GM groups around the world are demanding strict labelling on GM foods.

Should we continue to allow research and development of cloning and genetic modification?

A. The writer thinks that cloning and genetic modification have both benefits and concerns – "Although there are benefits, there are concerns..." List the benefits and concerns in the appropriate columns.

Benefit	Concern

It is unlikely that the development in cloning and genetic modification will stop, so how can these fields of science be made more acceptable to people?

_____

_____

_____

_____

ISBN: 978-1-897164-42-6

B. Read the clues and complete the crossword puzzle with words from the passage.

Across

A. about right and wrong
B. putting something under control and using it
C. those who don't eat meat or fish
D. poisonous substances
E. change
F. difficult situations for making decisions

Down

1. deformed, not having the form one is supposed to
2. unable to produce babies
3. helping to relax or feel better
4. not affected by
5. prohibited, barred
6. unborn babies in the early stage of development

ISBN: 978-1-897164-42-6

C. Imagine that "Ethics in Science: Cloning and Genetic Modification" is a news article. Write a letter to the editor expressing your view on the issue. You can be either for or against it. You don't have to give both sides of the argument.

ISBN: 978-1-897164-42-6

The World of Tea

After water, tea is the second most-consumed beverage in the world, and has been enjoyed for centuries. Tea production began in China, but soon spread to other parts of Asia. When European explorers, such as Marco Polo, came across the satisfying beverage on their travels, they sparked a demand for tea worldwide that continues to grow, in spite of competition from soft drinks and coffee.

There are four main types of tea: black, white, green, and oolong. The difference depends on the processes used for treating the tea leaves, such as oxidation, fermentation, heating, and drying. Black tea is withered, fully oxidized, and dried, and makes a strong, amber-coloured brew. English Breakfast and Darjeeling are popular black teas. Green tea is not oxidized; it is withered and then dried. It has a pale green/golden colour and a delicate taste. Oolong tea is in between black and green tea in colour and taste. Very popular in China, oolong is often referred to as the "Champagne of Teas". Do not drink it with milk, sugar, or lemon! White tea is the least processed. It is withered and dried by steaming. China and Japan produce the best green tea, Taiwan is known for its oolong tea, and India and Sri Lanka are famed for their black teas. Kenya, Argentina, and Vietnam are also major tea producers. The addition of spices, fruits, and flowers can also create different kinds of teas. In recent years, a market niche has been developed called "herbal teas" – chamomile and peppermint are popular – but these are not true teas as they do not derive from the plant *Camellia sinensis*.

Different regions have their own specialties. For example, Indian masala, or "chai" tea, is made with cardamom, ginger, cinnamon, fennel, and cloves. Mint tea is drunk in North Africa and the Middle East. Bubble tea, especially popular in Hong Kong, Taiwan, and Singapore, is tea mixed with cold milk and dollops of tapioca balls – a jelly-like substance. Earl Grey tea, named after a British prime minister who lived from 1764 to 1845 is, after English Breakfast tea, the most popular black tea in the world. It is a blend of black teas mixed with bergamot oil. Matcha, made from bright green powder, is the staple of the

ISBN: 978-1-897164-42-6

world-renowned Japanese tea ceremony. But now you can get it at popular coffee chain-stores. It is high in vitamins A, B, C, E, and K.

Tea balls are a new novelty tea, made by sewing the leaves and flowering parts of tea plants into tight pod-like balls. When the pod is placed in hot water, it opens up, revealing the lovely flower inside.

Versatile and healthy, tea deserves its place as the world's most loved beverage. Let's lift our glasses and have a toast – to tea!

A. Complete the chart below using what you have learned in the passage.

Types of Tea

Tea	Description
black	
white	
green	
oolong	

How many types of tea have you tried? Which one is your favourite? Why do you like it?

_____

_____

_____

_____

ISBN: 978-1-897164-42-6

B. Identify the types of special tea described.

1. This tea is named after a British prime minister. _____

2. There are cinnamon and cloves in this tea. _____

3. People like putting tapioca balls in this tea. _____

4. This tea is used in Japanese tea ceremonies. _____

C. Rewrite the following sentences in your own words while retaining the original meanings.

1. After water, tea is the second most-consumed beverage in the world, and has been enjoyed for centuries.

   _____

   _____

   _____

2. Very popular in China, oolong is often referred to as the "Champagne of Teas".

   _____

   _____

3. Versatile and healthy, tea deserves its place as the world's most loved beverage.

   _____

   _____

4. When European explorers, such as Marco Polo, came across the satisfying beverage on their travels, they sparked a demand for tea worldwide that continues to grow, in spite of competition from soft drinks and coffee.

   _____

   _____

   _____

ISBN: 978-1-897164-42-6

D. **Imagine that you are writing a feature on tea balls for a newsletter. Explain what they are and why they have become more and more popular. Search the Web for more information about tea balls. Include a few images, if possible.**

ISBN: 978-1-897164-42-6

Living with Robots

To a child, a robot is a toy, a clever plaything that looks a little bit human, but can also do amazing things. Children have loved robot-like toys for years. But robots are not just toys; they are being manufactured to do an assortment of tasks all over the world, such as in the manufacturing of automobiles, in security work such as dismantling bombs, and in the aerospace industry. At the moment, most people do not come into contact with robots on a regular basis, but this is changing. What is happening in Japan is a good case in point.

Japan has the world's most rapidly aging population, and its birthrate is declining. This means that, in the coming years, there will be a lot of elderly people there and not enough younger people to care for them. The government and the private sector in Japan recognize that this is a real problem and are working on ways to deal with it. One innovative solution relates to the manufacturing of robots.

Japan's industrial sector is busy creating appliances to make life more livable for those ever more numerous august years. In addition to robots designed for use in nursing homes – a response to the labour shortage in that sector – robot suits that help the aged stay mobile, and metre-tall speaking robots that act as parent-sitters for grown-up children, are some of the items in production. Some of these elderly-care devices have already gone mainstream. An "automatic washing device", manufactured initially for use in nursing homes, is now finding its place in salons and spas. Now anyone can go to a spa and hop into the clamshell-like machines that offer scented body shampoo and shower, with infrared steam and sound/aromatherapy. These robot-like machines will also apply a seaweed pack and finish off the treatment with a relaxing body-lotion massage.

ISBN: 978-1-897164-42-6

Almost half of the world's robot population lives in Japan. One could say, perhaps, that robots are fast becoming part of Japanese culture. Japan's Ministry of Economy, Trade and Industry has started an award program for "Robot of the Year". There are several categories: industrial robots (those used in painting and welding, for example), service robots (cleaning, security, elderly-care), special-environment robots (rescue), and robots developed by start-up firms. There is, of course, a grand prize as well.

Do you think these robots get excited when they find out they have been nominated?

A. Answer these questions.

1. Explain why the writer says, "What is happening in Japan is a good case in point."

_____

_____

2. Why are the Japanese so interested in developing robots?

_____

_____

3. Explain in your own words what "service robots" are.

_____

_____

Do you like being served by a robot? Why or why not?

_____

_____

_____

_____

_____

ISBN: 978-1-897164-42-6

B. Use no more than two sentences to summarize the main point of each of the following paragraphs.

1. Japan has the world's most rapidly aging population, and its birthrate is declining. This means that, in the coming years, there will be a lot of elderly people there and not enough younger people to care for them. The government and the private sector in Japan recognize that this is a real problem and are working on ways to deal with it. One innovative solution relates to the manufacturing of robots.

    _____

    _____

    _____

2. Apart from industrial use, robots can be educational. Robot kits are becoming more and more popular. They are kits made by manufacturers such as LEGO, Parallax, and Fischertechnik. Each kit is made up of plastic components and a mainboard so that children can build robots in different shapes and sizes, and with different functions. This helps stimulate children's creativity and interest in exploring science.

    _____

    _____

    _____

3. Robots are often used in bomb disposal, underwater tasks, mining, and for cleaning toxic waste. Hundreds of bomb disposal robots, for example, are being used in Iraq and Afghanistan by the U.S. military to defuse roadside bombs. In fact, robots are best used in environments which are unpleasant or dangerous for humans to work in. They never complain about the three-D work: dull, dirty, and dangerous.

    _____

    _____

    _____

    _____

ISBN: 978-1-897164-42-6

C. **Imagine a robotic suit that you designed to help the elderly move about more easily has won the Robot of the Year award. Explain to a group of elderly how it can help improve their quality of life.**

_____

_____

_____

_____

_____

_____

_____

_____

_____

_____

_____

_____

_____

_____

_____

_____

_____

_____

_____

_____

_____

ISBN: 978-1-897164-42-6

The Nobel Prizes

The bestowing of honours and awards is an activity that makes people stop and take note. In Canada, for instance, many people want to know who won the Stanley Cup in hockey or the Grey Cup in football. Those who love literature will want to know who won the Giller Prize or the Governor General's Awards. But few honours are newsworthy all over the world. Perhaps, more than any other honour, it is the Nobel Prizes which inspire the most respect and awe.

The Nobel Prize has been awarded for outstanding achievements in physics, chemistry, medicine, literature, and for work in peace since 1901. This all started when Alfred Nobel, a Swedish scientist, author, and pacifist, bequeathed his entire fortune upon his death in 1895 for this purpose. Alfred Nobel amassed a great fortune in his lifetime. He invented and held the patents for dynamite, blasting gelatin, and nitroglycerine, among other things.

To date, 768 individuals and 19 organizations have been awarded the Nobel Prize. Only 33 Nobel Laureates are women. Among these women, the renowned scientist Marie Curie won the Nobel Prize for Physics in 1903 for research into radiation phenomena. She and her husband Pierre Curie shared half the prize, and their senior colleague Antoine Henri Becquerel was awarded the other half for the discovery of radioactivity. In 1911, she was awarded the Nobel Prize for Chemistry for her discovery of radium and polonium. In 1935, Marie and Pierre Curie's daughter, Irène, was awarded the Nobel Prize for Chemistry along with her husband, Frédéric Joliot, "in recognition of their synthesis of new radioactive elements". In 1997, Canadian Jody Williams won the Nobel Peace Prize for her work as founding coordinator for the International Campaign to Ban Landmines. She shared the award, and the money that goes with it, with the ICBL organization itself.

ISBN: 978-1-897164-42-6

In addition to Marie Curie, there are five other multiple Nobel Laureates. The United Nations High Commissioner for Refugees was awarded the Nobel Peace Prize in 1954 and 1981. The International Committee of the Red Cross was awarded the same prize three times: in 1917, 1944, and 1963 – thereby becoming the most-awarded recipient. Linus Pauling was awarded the prize for Chemistry in 1954 for research into chemical bonding, and the peace prize in 1962. John Bardeen shared the physics prize with two colleagues in 1956 for research on semiconductors, and again in 1972 for research into superconductivity theory. Frederick Sanger was awarded the prize in chemistry in 1958 for research into the structure of proteins, and shared the prize with his colleague in 1980 for work in the DNA-sequencing of nucleic acids.

You can learn more about the inspiring stories of our Nobel Prize Laureates at **www.nobelprize.org**.

A. Complete the chart on the Nobel prizes below.

Achievement	Laureate	Year of Award
Discovery of radium and polonium		
Research into chemical bonding		
Research into radiation phenomena		
Synthesis of new radioactive elements		
Discovery of radioactivity		
Founding of International Campaign to Ban Landmines		
DNA-sequencing of nucleic acids		
Research on semiconductors		
Research into superconductivity theory		
Research into structure of proteins		

ISBN: 978-1-897164-42-6

The Nobel Prize has been awarded for outstanding achievements in physics, chemistry, medicine, literature, and for work in peace. If you were asked to add one more field for the Nobel Prize, which one would you consider? Why?

_____

_____

_____

_____

_____

B. In your own words, rewrite the following sentences from the passage. Keep the original meaning of each sentence.

1. In addition to Marie Curie, there are five other multiple Nobel Laureates.

_____

_____

_____

2. Perhaps, more than any other honour, it is the Nobel Prizes which inspire the most respect and awe.

_____

_____

3. The bestowing of honours and awards is an activity that makes people stop and take note.

_____

_____

4. This all started when Alfred Nobel, a Swedish scientist, author, and pacifist, bequeathed his entire fortune upon his death in 1895 for this purpose.

_____

_____

ISBN: 978-1-897164-42-6

C. Read the clues and complete the crossword puzzle with words from the passage.

Across

A. amazement

B. someone who thinks war and violence are wrong

C. accumulated

D. giving, presenting

E. award winners

F. well-known

G. those who work with you

Down

1. many

2. making one feel enthusiastic or interested

3. people forced to leave their homes or countries because of war

4. accomplishments

5. starting of an organization

ISBN: 978-1-897164-42-6

"Another Ice Age" on the Way?

Today, so many of the world's scientists and environmentalists are talking about global warming: the gradual and inexorable increase in the world's overall temperature due to increased carbon dioxide emissions and the resulting "greenhouse" effect. So it may seem odd that many of these same scientists and environmentalists are saying that global warming may bring about another Ice Age. How can this be?

Scientists refer to a time – from about 1300 to 1870 – when temperatures in parts of northern Europe and North America fell as "The Little Ice Age". Although the drop in temperature was only about 1°C, it caused significant hardship. For example, glaciers in Norway advanced onto farmland, and caused crop failures in other parts of Europe. This indicates just how much damage could be caused if temperatures should drop more steeply and more quickly – as they did during a much greater Ice Age 8200 years ago.

Scientists have theorized about this period of rapid cooling, which lasted about 100 years. We can still find evidence of this Ice Age today: the frozen bodies of woolly mammoths encased in the ice of Siberia. One plausible theory for this has to do with the warming effect of the Gulf Stream in the Atlantic Ocean – combined with the demise of North America's glacial reservoir, Lake Agassiz.

The Gulf Stream refers to a current of water in the Atlantic Ocean that moves up along the coast of North America

ISBN: 978-1-897164-42-6

to the North Atlantic basin. This current begins with warm water from the tropical southern regions of the ocean, cooling – and sinking – as it heads north. The current then heads south again along the ocean bottom, acting as a conveyor belt in a global system of ocean currents. The effect of this current of warm water is very powerful, helping to explain why there are certain islands along the coast of Scotland which have palm trees, and why the climate of Iceland is relatively mild despite its high latitude.

It has been theorized that Lake Agassiz, which covered much of inland North America (Lake Winnipeg is a remnant of that ancient inland "sea"), was drained when ice dams located in northeastern North America collapsed. Vast amounts of cold, fresh water began spilling into the warmer, salty Atlantic Ocean, causing the Gulf Stream "conveyor belt" and its warming effect on northern Europe to cease. While some scientists do not agree with this theory, it is important to remind ourselves that the glaciers of Greenland are melting at an unprecedented rate. If this continues, it may disrupt the Gulf Stream and cause another "Ice Age".

A. Based on the information in the passage, explain the cause or effect of the following.

1. Cause: _____

    _____

    Effect: There is a gradual and inexorable increase in the world's overall temperature.

2. Cause: There was a drop in temperature of about 1°C between 1300 and 1870.

    Effect: _____

    _____

3. Cause: _____

    _____

    Effect: The climate of Iceland is relatively mild despite its high latitude.

4. Cause: Vast amounts of cold, fresh water spilled into the warmer Atlantic Ocean.

    Effect: _____

    _____

ISBN: 978-1-897164-42-6

B. Read the clues and complete the crossword puzzle with words from the passage.

Across

A. stop

B. large masses of slow-moving ice

C. what is left over

D. people who work to preserve the natural environment

Down

1. developed a set of ideas to help explain something

2. cannot be prevented from continuing

3. end, death

4. never happened before

5. completely covered

6. release of gases

ISBN: 978-1-897164-42-6

C. **Based on the following points, write about the effects of global warming on the ecosystem.**

- some species forced out of their habitats (possibly to extinction)
- some species may flourish
- changes in timing of life patterns such as annual migration dates
- may alter regional predator-prey balance
- ocean pH lowering as a result of increased carbon dioxide levels; a damaging effect on coral reefs
- melting polar ice threatening the survival of polar bears
- polar bears use sea ice to reach their prey
- ice now further separate; dead polar bears found in the water, believed to have drowned

_____

_____

_____

_____

_____

_____

_____

_____

_____

_____

_____

_____

_____

ISBN: 978-1-897164-42-6

Special Olympians

For millions of people around the world, the Olympic Games are an exciting event, and greatly anticipated. Whether it is winter or summer, the world becomes united every two years in their enthusiasm and admiration for the world's greatest athletes. We remember the names of many of them, even those whose achievements occurred half a century ago: Jesse Owens, who won four gold medals for the United States at the Berlin Olympics in 1936; the "Flying Dutchwoman" Fanny Blankers-Koen who, as a 30-year-old mother of two, won four gold medals at the London Olympics in 1948. There's Richard Fosbury, who invented a new way to do the high jump, by jumping over the bar head first at the 1968 Olympic Games. His "Fosbury Flop" soon became the conventional method of clearing the bar. Gaetan Boucher, Brian Orser, Marnie McBean, Mark Tewksbury, and Cindy Klassen are just a few of Canada's medal-winners in recent years, and their names are familiar.

But here are some names of Olympians you may not have heard of: three-time medal-winner Tahir Ahmed, from Pakistan; three-time medal-winner Latisha Ferguson, from Bahamas; three-time medal-winner Amita Shrestha, from Nepal. They all participated in the Special Olympics.

The Special Olympics is an international organization that helps people with intellectual disabilities become physically fit, and compete at the elite level in an international forum. It was founded in 1968 by Eunice Kennedy Shriver, a sister of former American president John F. Kennedy. The first event was held in Chicago, Illinois, that year. In addition to the Special Olympics World Summer and Winter Games, which alternate every two years, the Special Olympics provides athletic training for more than 2.25 million children in over 150 countries. Athletes must be at least eight years old to participate, and be identified by an agency or professional as having intellectual disabilities, cognitive delays, or significant learning or vocational problems due to cognitive delay.

Children and adults who participate in Special Olympics develop improved physical fitness and motor skills, greater self-confidence and a more positive self-image. They grow mentally,

ISBN: 978-1-897164-42-6

socially, and spiritually. They also enjoy the rewards of friendship and ultimately discover not only new abilities and talents but also "their voices".

The Special Olympic Games are usually held after the Olympic Games. Next time you are finished cheering on the great Olympic athletes of the summer or winter Olympians, make an effort to find the channel that broadcasts the Special Olympic World Games – and keep on cheering!

The Special Olympics Athlete Oath:
"Let me win. But if I cannot win, let me be brave in the attempt."

A. Answer these questions.

1. Explain briefly what "Fosbury Flop" is.

_____

_____

2. Who are eligible for taking part in the Special Olympics?

_____

_____

3. Apart from the difference in participants, what is one other major difference between the Olympics and the Special Olympics?

_____

_____

Do you think the Special Olympics Athlete Oath is equally applicable to whatever we do? Why or why not?

_____

_____

_____

_____

71

ISBN: 978-1-897164-42-6

17

B. Give a derivative of each of the following words from the passage. Use it in a sentence of your own to show its meaning.

1. anticipated: _____

_____

_____

2. admiration: _____

_____

_____

3. disabilities: _____

_____

_____

4. compete: _____

_____

_____

5. alternate: _____

_____

_____

6. athletic: _____

_____

_____

7. socially: _____

_____

_____

8. brave: _____

_____

_____

ISBN: 978-1-897164-42-6

C.

C. Read the following article and in no more than 80 words, make a summary of how the Special Olympics came about. Your summary should include only the main ideas and leave out the details.

The concept of Special Olympics was conceived by Eunice Kennedy Shriver, who then started a day camp for children with intellectual disabilities at her home in 1962.

Shriver believed that people with intellectual disabilities were far more capable than commonly believed and deserving of the same opportunities and experiences as others. So, in June 1962, she invited 35 boys and girls with intellectual disabilities to Camp Shriver, a day camp at Timberlawn, her home in Maryland, to explore their capabilities in a variety of sports and physical activities. Using Camp Shriver as a pilot project, Shriver promoted the concept of involvement in physical activity and competition opportunities for people with intellectual disabilities. Camp Shriver then became an annual event.

In 1963, the Kennedy Foundation supported 11 similar camps around the United States. By 1969, the Foundation supported 32 camps across the country that served more than 10 000 children with intellectual disabilities. The movement grew beyond the Kennedy Foundation, and between 1963 and 1968, more than 300 camps similar to Camp Shriver were started.

The Special Olympics movement got its start on July 20, 1968 when the First International Special Olympic Games were held in Chicago, U.S.A.

ISBN: 978-1-897164-42-6

The Story of "Room to Read"

John Wood was a busy business executive who spent most of his time working hard for Microsoft as Regional Director for the Asia-Pacific region. In 1998, John decided he needed a vacation, and chose the mountains of Nepal for some hiking and solitude. Along the way, he met a man whose job was to inspect the schools in the area. His job title was "Education Resource Officer", and he invited John to visit a school. John was saddened to discover that the school had few educational resources. In fact, the few books the school had – including old travel guides and a romance novel left behind by foreign travellers – were kept locked away like treasured items! When John left the village, the school principal had a simple request: "Perhaps, Sir, someday you will come back with books." John said he would.

When he got to a computer café, John e-mailed friends around the world, asking them to send old children's books to his parents' home in Colorado, U.S.A. John thought maybe he would get around 200 books. A few weeks later, John received an urgent e-mail from Colorado – there were at least 3000 books filling up the family garage and they were quickly running out of room! John was thrilled, but he also knew he had a few problems that needed to be solved. For one thing, he needed to get those books to the school in Nepal! John kept his promise. A year later, he and his father Woody returned to the school with a yak, loaded down with huge sacks of books.

John had a more personal problem he needed to solve. For a while, he had felt there was something missing. He was a successful businessman, but he felt a compelling urge to do something different. His experience in Nepal made him realize that he had to quit his job and make helping the world's poor children his life's mission. So this is what he did.

Some people didn't think he was making the right decision and tried to get him to change his mind. But he remembered something his dad, Woody, told him when he was in junior high school. Woody had asked his son if he'd

ISBN: 978-1-897164-42-6

be joining the school football team. John began to cry because he didn't want to play – yet he didn't want to disappoint his dad either. Then Woody said, "Don't do anything to please us. Do what you think is the right thing to do and get used to answering only to yourself."

He set up a charity called Room to Read in 2000. Today, Room to Read has changed the lives of hundreds of thousands of children by building schools and libraries, and funding girls' scholarships in Nepal, Vietnam, Cambodia, India, Sri Lanka, and Laos. They will soon be starting programs in South Africa and Latin America. John wants to help 10 million children. His story so far tells us that he – and all the people who have shared his dream – will succeed.

A. In your own words, write the main idea of each paragraph of *The Story of "Room to Read"*.

Paragraph One _____

_____

Paragraph Two _____

_____

Paragraph Three _____

_____

Paragraph Four _____

_____

Paragraph Five _____

_____

 **Would you have quit your job as what John Wood had done if you were a businessman as successful as he? Why or why not?**

_____

_____

_____

_____

ISBN: 978-1-897164-42-6

B. **Complete the crossword puzzle with derivatives of the clue words.**

Across	Down
A. educational	1. invite
B. mission	2. solve
C. simple	3. problems
D. charity	4. solitude
E. disappoint	5. guides

ISBN: 978-1-897164-42-6

C. **Imagine you are John Wood. Write an e-mail to your friends about your plan of helping underprivileged children around the world.**

File Edit View Go Favorites Tools Window Help

Back | Forward | Stop | Refresh | Home | Search | Favorites | Media | History | Mail | Print | Edit

Address | www.popularworld.com | Go

To: _____

Cc: _____ Bcc: _____

Subject: _____

ISBN: 978-1-897164-42-6

ISBN: 978-1-897164-42-6

Section 2
Grammar

ISBN 978-1-897164-42-6

1 Verbs with Prepositions

There are some verbs that need to be used together with prepositions.

Example: His teacher talks him after school every day. (✗)

His teacher <u>talks to</u> him after school every day. (✔)

Some verbs take an object, followed by a particular preposition.

Example: They <u>accused him of</u> stealing their soccer ball.

A. Complete the sentences with suitable prepositions.

1. This is what we've been hoping _____ .

2. She agreed _____ me _____ the action to take.

3. Who told you that I didn't care _____ the outcome?

4. Don't laugh _____ the poor little boy.

5. He asked me _____ help but I turned him _____ .

6. Have you heard _____ a teacher called Sam Brown?

7. He always complains _____ not having enough support.

8. She was unable to borrow _____ the bank.

9. He walked so carelessly that he bumped _____ a pole.

10. Angelina vowed that she would never speak _____ me again.

11. They insisted _____ inviting him to the meeting.

12. Last night I dreamed _____ an exciting safari.

13. My brother has applied _____ the company _____ a trainee position.

14. I don't think I can rely _____ him.

15. The shop assistant explained it _____ me in detail.

ISBN: 978-1-897164-42-6

B. Write the preposition that goes with each of the following verbs.

1. belong _____
2. listen _____
3. sympathize _____
4. hint _____
5. lead _____
6. consist _____
7. scoff _____
8. stare _____
9. depend _____
10. refer _____
11. side _____
12. glance _____

C. Write sentences to show the difference in meaning of each of the following verbs when used with different prepositions.

1. result from   result in

_____

_____

2. fight for   fight against

_____

_____

3. suffer from   suffer with

_____

_____

4. appeal to   appeal for

_____

_____

5. wait for   wait on

_____

_____

ISBN: 978-1-897164-42-6

1 Verbs with Prepositions

Phrasal Verbs

A **phrasal verb** is a verb used with an adverb or preposition. It either extends the usual meaning of the verb or creates a new meaning.

Examples: The children were <u>looking at</u> me as if I were a stranger.

The children were <u>looking after</u> the injured kitten. *(taking care of)*

D. Complete the following groups of sentences with suitable phrasal verbs.

1. stand

   a. Mr. Watson _____ as Chairman because he failed to win the board's support.

   b. What does "UNESCO" _____ ?

   c. Ms. Kelly _____ for Mr. Walsh, who injured his right foot while skiing last weekend.

   d. The firefighters had to _____ because of the hurricane.

2. get

   a. Mavis doesn't seem to _____ with the new student.

   b. "Don't waste any more time. Let's _____ business," said the manager.

   c. We must not let the matter bog us down. We should _____ it instead and look ahead.

3. talk

   a. Instead of admitting his wrong, Jeff _____ to the teacher.

   b. He tried to _____ her _____ buying the expensive jewel.

   c. Terry managed to _____ Beth _____ going there with him.

ISBN: 978-1-897164-42-6

E. Write sentences to show the meanings of each family of phrasal verbs. You may use different tenses.

1. break in; break up; break out; break down

   _____

   _____

   _____

   _____

2. put up with; put off; put...down; put aside

   _____

   _____

   _____

   _____

3. come about; come up with; come along; come forward

   _____

   _____

   _____

   _____

4. make off with; make up; make up for; make out

   _____

   _____

   _____

   _____

ISBN: 978-1-897164-42-6

2 Non-finite Verbs

A **finite verb** is a verb that agrees with its subject. A **non-finite verb** is one that does not have to agree with the subject.

Examples: Samantha <u>*enjoys*</u> playing in the snow. (finite verb)

<u>*To play*</u> in the snow, Samantha needs to dress warmly. (infinitive; non-finite verb)

Participles, gerunds, and infinitives are all non-finite verbs.

A. In the following paragraph, write the types of non-finite verbs above the underlined words.

Adrian loves <u>designing</u> clothes. Back in October, he had already started <u>to plan</u> his outfits for his Christmas parties. Because his elder sister taught him how <u>to sew</u>, he knows how <u>to make</u> costumes. When he is not <u>doing</u> homework or <u>studying</u>, he helps his drama teacher design costumes for the annual school play. On weekends, he enjoys <u>buying</u> different types of fabric with his sister. From <u>choosing</u> colours to <u>putting</u> everything together, Adrian always finds something new <u>to learn</u>. Sometimes he gets a little <u>exhausted</u> from <u>running</u> all over the place <u>to find</u> the right material, but he loves his hobby all the same.

Now that there is less homework because the holiday is near, he has more time <u>to spend</u> on his own project: he is <u>making</u> himself a Nutcracker costume for the party with his cousins.

ISBN: 978-1-897164-42-6

Participles

Both **present** and **past participles** can function as adjectives.

Examples: <u>Working</u> mothers often tire out at the end of the day.

The <u>worried</u> mother took her baby to the clinic.

B. Complete the following sentences with participles of the verbs given. Decide whether the present or past participle should be used.

1. The _____ (exhaust) players sat quietly in the bullpen.

2. We haven't played with the _____ (win) team this season.

3. _____ (speed) motorists will be stopped and fined.

4. _____ (frighten) by the fierce dog, the stranger ran away.

5. _____ (surround) by her fans, the pop star promised to sing a song from her latest album.

6. The three children _____ (run) on the track are from Mrs. Sutherland's class.

7. The _____ (rise) temperature fuelled the drought and made the farmers' lives even more miserable.

8. _____ (satisfy) with Ben's results, Ms. Watts agreed to let Ben join her team.

9. The _____ (excite) news took everyone by surprise.

10. The _____ (trap) kitten trembled with fear and waited desperately for help.

11. The _____ (finish) paintings will be on display in the library for two months.

12. The _____ (entertain) show lasted almost two hours.

ISBN: 978-1-897164-42-6

2 Non-finite Verbs

Gerunds

Gerunds look like present participles, but they function as nouns.

Examples: <u>*Diving*</u> *is fun but it is an activity that requires* <u>*training*</u>.
(as subject)   (as object)

C. Rewrite the following sentences by replacing the underlined nouns with gerunds. Make any other necessary changes.

1. <u>A loss</u> in the eighth inning upset the game plan.

    _____

2. <u>A laugh</u> relieves stress and lifts your mood.

    _____

3. <u>An increase in</u> the use of fuel leads to more pollution.

    _____

4. He sustained severe injury as a result of <u>the fall</u> from the horse.

    _____

    _____

5. <u>A jump</u> over the ditch can be dangerous.

    _____

    _____

Infinitives

In most cases, an **infinitive** goes with "to". In some cases, it can be used without "to". Infinitives without "to" are called **bare infinitives**. Infinitives can function as nouns.

Examples: *They wanted* <u>*to talk*</u> *to the owner of the restaurant.*

He did not let us <u>*watch*</u> *the game.*

ISBN: 978-1-897164-42-6

D. Complete the following sentences with infinitives. Add any other details you feel are needed to make the meaning complete.

1. Everyone at the party was trying to _____

2. I was shocked to _____

3. To _____ , we had to seek help from the committee members.

4. To _____ would be a challenge for all of us.

5. The doctor would like to _____

6. What I want to do most is to _____

7. We stayed until the show was over to _____

8. They watched the robber _____

E. Compose a short paragraph using the following verbs as participles, gerunds, or infinitives.

surprise	applaud	worry	win	lose

_____

_____

_____

_____

_____

_____

_____

_____

_____

ISBN: 978-1-897164-42-6

3 More on Adjectives

Order of Adjectives

When we use a number of adjectives together, we need to place them in order, based on the function of each of the adjectives. The usual order is: value, size, age, shape, colour, origin, material.

Value	delicious, lovely, charming
Size	small, huge, tiny
Age	old, young
Shape	round, square, rectangular
Colour	red, blonde, black
Origin	Canadian, American, European
Material	plastic, wooden, silver

Example: *Ming is a little, beautiful Asian girl.* (✗)
Ming is a beautiful, little Asian girl. (✔)

A. Arrange the order of the following groups of adjectives.

1. a house (wooden, small, old)

   _____

2. the dots (yellow, little, round, bright)

   _____

3. a lady (charming, Canadian, tall)

   _____

4. an ornament (silver, exquisite, attractive)

   _____

5. the athlete (young, well-built)

   _____

6. the shirt (soiled, blue, old)

   _____

7. a chair (brown, antique, wooden)

   _____

ISBN: 978-1-897164-42-6

B. Rewrite the sentences where the order of the adjectives is wrong.

1. After an hour's walk, we finally reached a small, beautiful old chapel.

   _____

2. According to Jenny, the new teacher is a witty lanky gentleman in his late thirties.

   _____

3. They showed me an oval, sparkling big gemstone.

   _____

4. Mr. Buffet bought her a silk, black new scarf.

   _____

5. The setting sun is one huge, dazzling red fireball.

   _____

6. She likes wearing that pink, leather tight coat.

   _____

C. Enrich each of the following sentences by using at least two adjectives to describe the underlined noun.

1. I met a girl at Beth's birthday party.

   _____

2. They found a hut deep in the forest.

   _____

3. The truck finally came to a halt.

   _____

4. The banner caught our attention.

   _____

5. The goose came towards us.

   _____

ISBN: 978-1-897164-42-6

3   More on Adjectives

Using Adjectives for Comparison

To compare people, places, events, or things when there is no difference, we can use the structure "as + adjective + as".

Example: *I think I'm* <u>*as tall as*</u> *you.*

To make a comparison when there is a difference, we can use the structure "not as/ so + adjective + as".

Example: *The Eiffel Tower is* <u>*not as tall as*</u> *the CN Tower.*

D. Write two sentences using "as + adjective + as" and two using "not as/so + adjective + as".

1.   as...as

   a. _____

   b. _____

2.   not so/as...as

   a. _____

   b. _____

Comparisons of Quantity

To show difference, we can use "more", "less", or "fewer" + "than". To show no difference, we can use "as much as", "as many as", "as few as", or "as little as".

E. Write sentences with the following.

1.   more...than

   _____

   _____

2.   less...than

   _____

ISBN: 978-1-897164-42-6

3. fewer...than

_____

4. as much as

_____

5. as many as

_____

6. as few as

_____

7. as little as

_____

 Position of Adjectives
. . . .

We usually put adjectives in front of nouns that they describe. For some adjectives, however, they can be placed after the nouns, but the change in positioning would change their meanings.

F. **Explain the difference in meaning of each underlined adjective when used before and after the noun it describes.**

1. a. The people <u>concerned</u> did not raise any objection.
    b. The <u>concerned</u> parents rushed to the school to find out what had happened.

    a. _____   b. _____

2. a. The members <u>present</u> all voted for the motion.
    b. The <u>present</u> situation worries me.

    a. _____   b. _____

3. a. He is a <u>responsible</u> person.
    b. The officer <u>responsible</u> for the case was away.

    a. _____   b. _____

ISBN: 978-1-897164-42-6

4 More on Adverbs

Interrogative Adverbs

"When", "Why", "Where", and "How" are **interrogative adverbs**. They are usually placed at the beginning of a question.

Examples: <u>How</u> *did he manage to get away with it?*

<u>When</u> *will the report be ready for discussion?*

<u>Why</u> *did he miss the train?*

<u>Where</u> *is the library?*

A. Write questions that elicit the given responses.

1. _____

_____

Pull this starter and you can start the engine.

2. _____

_____

I got it from a corner store near my home.

3. _____

It took me about an hour to complete it.

4. _____

The flight had been delayed because of the snowstorm; I arrived on Sunday instead of Saturday.

5. _____

It cost me $50, much cheaper than I'd expected.

6. _____

He seldom goes to the supermarket, once a week at the most.

7. _____

They didn't show up because they thought the show had been cancelled.

8. _____

Frankly, I don't have confidence in completing it on time; we just do our best.

ISBN: 978-1-897164-42-6

Relative Adverbs

"Where", "when", and "why" can also be used to join sentences or clauses. They are often used in place of the more formal structure of "preposition + which" in a relative clause.

Examples: *That is the room <u>where</u> the exhibits were placed.*
(in which)

You should let your parents know <u>why</u> you stayed after school.
(the reason for which)

There was a time <u>when</u> everyone was about to give up.
(at which)

B. Join the sentences with the appropriate relative adverbs. Make any other necessary changes.

1. This is the auditorium. They ran the seminars.

   _____

2. The principal did not understand it. She declined the offer.

   _____

3. They are planning to build a park. The old church once stood on the site.

   _____

4. Mr. Sutherland came at a time. They were having a heated debate.

   _____

5. The police wanted to know. She had not come forward earlier.

   _____

6. They had a trip in the summer. In that summer, I was in South Africa.

   _____

7. We met at the café. Margaret worked at the café.

   _____

8. He explained it to his parents. He wanted to leave for Rome.

   _____

ISBN: 978-1-897164-42-6

4 More on Adverbs

Adverbs for Expressing Opinions and Viewpoints

Some adverbs and adverbial expressions help us express our viewpoint or opinion about an action, or make some comment on the action.

Example: <u>I feel strongly that</u> you should consider withdrawing from the contest.
<u>Seriously</u>, you should consider withdrawing from the contest.

C. **Rewrite each of the following sentences by using an adverb to express a viewpoint or an opinion. Make any other necessary changes.**

1. I was surprised that he turned out to be the winner.

   _____

2. In an ideal situation, we would have at least 18 months for the project.

   _____

3. To be honest with you, I can't think of any solutions to this problem.

   _____

4. I have no doubt that she is the best person to take up the assignment.

   _____

5. It is obvious that Mrs. Kennedy will continue to coach the team.

   _____

6. The plan doesn't work if we look at it from an economic point of view.

   _____

7. It is apparent that Ms. Fields did not know anything about it.

   _____

8. In theory, the waste can be recycled and reused.

   _____

   _____

ISBN: 978-1-897164-42-6

Commenting Adverbs

These are very similar to adverbs for expressing viewpoints and opinions. In fact, they are often the same words, but they go in a different position – after the verb to be or before the main verb.

Example: *He is the most qualified candidate for this job.*

He is <u>certainly</u> the most qualified candidate for this job.

D. Add an appropriate commenting adverb to each of the following sentences.

1. It is the most exciting playoff game we have ever had.

   _____

2. He never got a chance to explain what had happened.

   _____

3. It was a mistake to entrust the work to the new staff.

   _____

4. We had to stay put here for the night.

   _____

5. You liked Priscilla's performance.

   _____

6. They suffered a most humiliating loss.

   _____

7. The guests had a wonderful time and the host was delighted.

   _____

8. Mr. Greene is not happy with our reluctance.

   _____

9. What she did was beyond our imagination.

   _____

10. They were elated to learn that they had been nominated for the award.

   _____

ISBN: 978-1-897164-42-6

5   Compound Words

We often find adjectives and nouns combined into compound structures in a variety of ways. In general, there are three forms of **compound words**:
- the closed form
  Example: keyboard
- the hyphenated form
  Example: a fifty-six-page book
- the open form
  Example: new year

A. **Write five compound words for each of the following categories.**

Closed	Hyphenated	Open

B. **Decide whether the underlined part of each of the following sentences is a compound word or simply a case of word modified by an adjective. Write "COM" for a compound word.**

1. There is a <u>post office</u> in the lighthouse in Peggy's Cove.   _____

2. Jason's brother has got himself a <u>flashy sportscar</u>.   _____

3. The <u>high school</u> is just a block away from our school.   _____

4. Many children are somehow allergic to <u>peanut butter</u>.   _____

5. The <u>audio signal</u> was so weak that it could hardly be picked up.   _____

6. The little children enjoyed their time at the <u>petting zoo</u>.   _____

7. There are a lot of <u>tall buildings</u> along the lakeshore area.   _____

ISBN: 978-1-897164-42-6

The Hyphenated Form

Many compound words are hyphenated.

Example: a ten-year-old boy

Note, however, that when the modifying words come after the noun, they should not be hyphenated.

Example: The ten-year-old boy turned out to be nine years and ten months old.

C. **Rewrite the following sentences by combining the modifying words with the nouns to form compound words. Make any other necessary changes.**

1. My uncle owns a farm that is six acres in area.

   _____

   _____

2. The developer has decided to construct a building that is twenty storeys high.

   _____

3. The door, which is fire resistant, looks similar to the other doors in the same building.

   _____

4. The road that leads to the cathedral is lined with trees.

   _____

5. Mr. Saunders managed to secure a loan which is interest free.

   _____

6. We were greatly disappointed by his performance, which was way below average.

   _____

7. The project, which cost a million dollars, was completed on schedule.

   _____

8. Although the meeting lasted four hours, nothing was accomplished.

   _____

ISBN: 978-1-897164-42-6

5 Compound Words

D. Create hyphenated compound words and use them in sentences of your own.

1. _____

2. _____

3. _____

4. _____

5. _____

6. _____

Compound Plurals

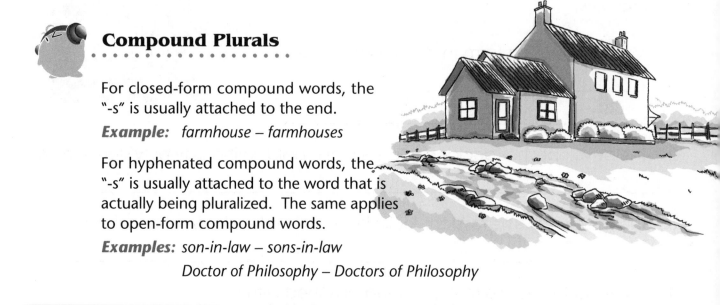

For closed-form compound words, the "-s" is usually attached to the end.

Example: *farmhouse – farmhouses*

For hyphenated compound words, the "-s" is usually attached to the word that is actually being pluralized. The same applies to open-form compound words.

Examples: *son-in-law – sons-in-law*

Doctor of Philosophy – Doctors of Philosophy

E. Write the plural form of the following compound words.

1. vice-principal _____

2. sergeant major _____

3. man-hour _____

4. master of ceremony _____

5. family name _____

6. lady-in-waiting _____

7. bill of fare _____

8. teacher librarian _____

9. gateway _____

10. editor-in-chief _____

11. winter festival _____

12. merry-go-round _____

ISBN: 978-1-897164-42-6

F. See if the following compound words are written in the proper way. Rewrite the improper ones. Consult a dictionary when in doubt.

1. worldwide _____

2. wellbeing _____

3. year end _____

4. extra-ordinary _____

5. also ran _____

6. forget-me-not _____

7. prime minister _____

8. blood pressure _____

9. wax-museum _____

10. homeoffice _____

11. inhouse _____

12. under developed _____

Compound Words with Prefixes

Compound words with prefixes are usually in closed form.

Examples: *town – downtown, midtown, uptown*

G. Write three compound words for each of the following prefixes.

1. extra _____

2. inter _____

3. semi _____

4. super _____

5. anti _____

6. non _____

7. multi _____

8. over _____

ISBN: 978-1-897164-42-6

6 Frequently Confused Words

There are some words that we get easily confused with because they either sound the same or they have similar spellings. When in doubt, we should look up the word in a dictionary to make sure that we are using the right word.

Example: *The town is <u>further</u> away than I thought.* (✗)

The town is <u>farther</u> away than I thought. (✔)

A. Decide which word to use for each of the following sentences. Then use the other word in a sentence of your own to show its meaning.

1. advice   advise

   I should have heeded his _____ and stayed out of trouble.

   _____

2. affect   effect

   He didn't seem to see how it would _____ him.

   _____

3. all ready   already

   They told me that they had watched the movie _____ .

   _____

4. all together   altogether

   There are _____ seven boys and five girls on the team.

   _____

5. among   between

   The 12 children wanted to share the snacks _____ them.

   _____

6. sew   sow

   They will _____ the seeds when the snow melts.

   _____

ISBN: 978-1-897164-42-6

7. altar   alter

They did not intend to _____ their original plan.

_____

8. site   sight

We all laughed at the _____ of him in the funny costume.

_____

9. raise   rise

Please _____ your hand before you speak.

_____

B. Underline the wrongly used words in the following text. Replace them with the correct ones.

Kurt felt badly about what he'd done. He and Greg had been best friends until the day he accused Greg of stealing his video game and refused to except Greg's explanation that the game was a presence from Greg's uncle. Kurt kept calling Greg a thief from than on.

Last Friday when Kurt's mother tidied his room for him, she uncovered Kurt's "stolen" video game under his bed, between the many other books and toys. She said to Kurt, "I think you should apologize to Greg. Beside, you should make sure not to jump to a conclusion too soon." Kurt decided to go to Greg and make up with him.

You are a thief!

ISBN: 978-1-897164-42-6

6 Frequently Confused Words

C. Read the clues and complete the crossword puzzle below.

Across

A. go before

B. an early version of our writing

C. cover or surround completely

D. show appreciation

E. growing thick and healthy

F. We put a letter in this.

G. a strong current of air

Down

1. comfortable and expensive

2. do not know the whereabouts of something

3. go well with another thing

4. not tight

5. of an acceptable standard

6. moving downward

7. go on

ISBN: 978-1-897164-42-6

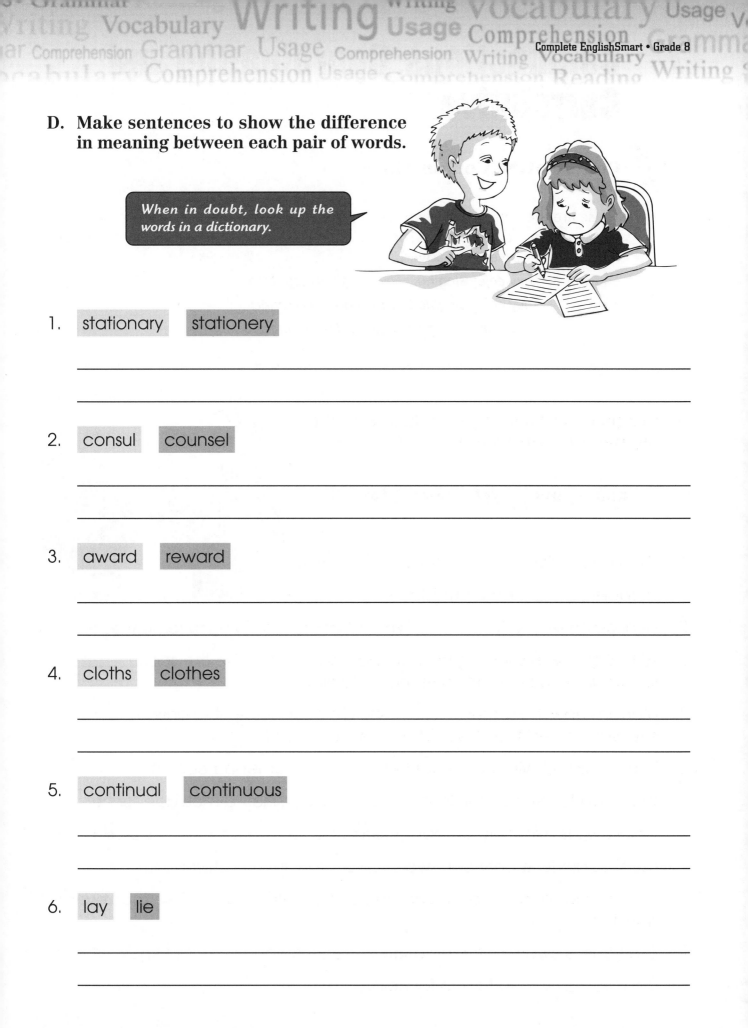

D. **Make sentences to show the difference in meaning between each pair of words.**

When in doubt, look up the words in a dictionary.

1. stationary   stationery

   _____

   _____

2. consul   counsel

   _____

   _____

3. award   reward

   _____

   _____

4. cloths   clothes

   _____

   _____

5. continual   continuous

   _____

   _____

6. lay   lie

   _____

   _____

ISBN: 978-1-897164-42-6

7 Conjunctions: Coordinating and Correlative

Coordinating Conjunctions

These are the conjunctions we are familiar with. They are used to join clauses to make compound sentences. They are also used to join other equal structures such as nouns, adjectives, and adverbs.

Examples: *They enjoy singing. They don't like dancing.*

They enjoy singing <u>but</u> *they don't like dancing.*

They drove along the long <u>and</u> *winding road.*

A. Complete the following sentences with the appropriate coordinating conjunctions.

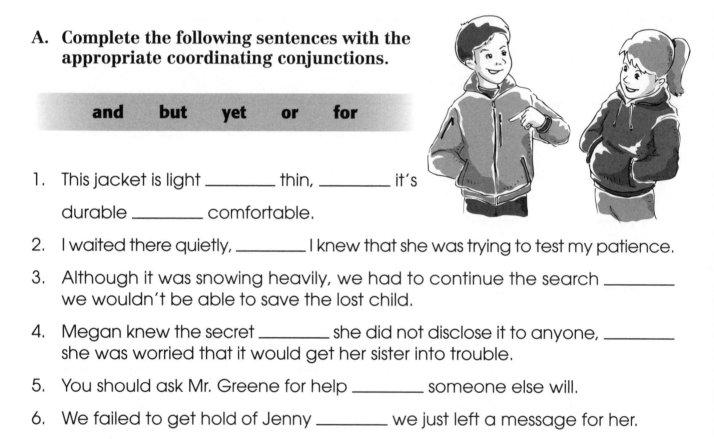

and	but	yet	or	for

1. This jacket is light _____ thin, _____ it's durable _____ comfortable.

2. I waited there quietly, _____ I knew that she was trying to test my patience.

3. Although it was snowing heavily, we had to continue the search _____ we wouldn't be able to save the lost child.

4. Megan knew the secret _____ she did not disclose it to anyone, _____ she was worried that it would get her sister into trouble.

5. You should ask Mr. Greene for help _____ someone else will.

6. We failed to get hold of Jenny _____ we just left a message for her.

7. Mrs. Lewis is available on both Tuesday _____ Friday, _____ she can meet us anytime between two _____ four in the afternoon.

8. They decided to invite Dr. Benton _____ Mrs. Walsh to be the keynote speaker.

9. Everyone is aware of the situation _____ no one seems to know what to do _____ who to turn to for help.

ISBN: 978-1-897164-42-6

B. Combine the following groups of sentences using coordinating conjunctions. Make any other necessary changes.

1. The committee members were divided on this matter. They agreed that it had to be settled as soon as possible. They wanted to invite an accountant to study it.

   _____

   _____

   _____

2. The project is scheduled to be completed by the end of this month. Many issues remain unresolved. A delay seems inevitable.

   _____

   _____

   _____

3. They are given two options. They can call off the match. They can play the game after school. They have to let the principal know their decision before noon.

   _____

   _____

   _____

4. By the time we reached the resort, everyone was exhausted. The first thing we wanted to do was to take a shower and go to bed. Before doing that, we had to wait for our leader to allocate our rooms.

   _____

   _____

   _____

5. Apparently the sign pointed to southeast. We followed it. We reached a deserted place. It was not the town indicated on the map.

   _____

   _____

   _____

ISBN: 978-1-897164-42-6

7 Conjunctions: Coordinating and Correlative

Correlative Conjunctions

These conjunctions have to go in pairs. The common **correlative conjunctions** include "either...or", "neither...nor", "not only...but also", and "whether...or". Note that when "either" is used without "or" and "neither" is used without "nor", they function as adjectives or pronouns.

Examples: <u>Either</u> player can take his place. *(adjective)*
<u>Either</u> of the players can take his place. *(pronoun)*
<u>Either</u> Josh <u>or</u> Benjamin can take his place. *(correlative conjunction)*
<u>Neither</u> plan is acceptable. *(adjective)*
<u>Neither</u> of the plans is acceptable. *(pronoun)*
<u>Neither</u> your plan <u>nor</u> Sadaf's plan is acceptable. *(correlative conjunction)*

C. **Complete the following sentences with correlative conjunctions.**

1. The coach remarked that _____ Jim _____ Matt could make a good left fielder.

2. The panel would consider _____ the scores _____ their performance in the interview.

3. _____ we go on the trip _____ not depends on my father, as he may not be able to take an extended leave.

4. You can get _____ a backpack _____ a pair of running shoes but you can't have both.

5. _____ Nelly _____ Fiona could describe precisely what had happened.

6. They are given a week to decide _____ to work part-time _____ full-time.

7. We are stuck with a plan that takes us _____ here _____ there. I wish someone could come up with a better plan.

8. He thinks that the principal will most likely choose _____ Peter _____ Dan to be the team leader.

9. _____ the show was great, _____ the fireworks were _____ spectacular.

10. Only the doctor can tell you _____ you can be discharged _____ not.

ISBN: 978-1-897164-42-6

D. Read the following sentences and decide if they are correct. Rewrite the incorrect sentences.

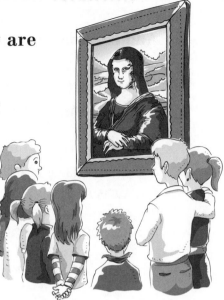

1. This painting not only is artistic but also it is priceless.

   _____
   _____

2. The coach couldn't make up his mind whether or not to change the pitcher.

   _____
   _____

3. I don't think neither Greg nor Paul should be held responsible for the mistake. They were there only as helpers.

   _____

4. Not only he lied but he also took away the books from the library.

   _____

5. She said that she would give you either a call or send you an e-mail to explain everything.

   _____

E. Write sentences with the following correlative conjunctions.

1. whether...or

   _____

2. either...or

   _____

3. neither...nor

   _____

4. not only...but also

   _____

ISBN: 978-1-897164-42-6

8   A Review on Punctuation

A. Add commas, semicolons, or colons in appropriate places.

1. They had one common goal to be able to complete the project by the end of the month.

2. By the time we reached the station the train had already departed and there was only one way to make it in time take a cab to go all the way to Townsville.

3. Everyone was taken by surprise they did not know what to do next.

4. He let Mr. Belinsky read his script it was the first script that he wrote.

5. Gary sensed that something had gone wrong the dogs were barking fiercely.

6. The committee was made up of the following members Mrs. Saunders the librarian Ms. Stewart the school secretary Mr. Dole our vice-principal.

7. Photosynthesis is the synthesis of sugar from light carbon dioxide and water oxygen is generated as a waste product.

8. They came up with a contingency plan enlist the help from the neighbouring schools.

9. We tried to dissuade him from doing it he went ahead anyway.

10. Before leaving make sure all the lights are turned off it is the least you can do to conserve energy.

11. He did not admit his mistake that he had forgotten to make payment on time.

12. The organizers hope to raise enough funds for the research fifty thousand dollars at least.

13. Because of the storm we cancelled the trip I was a little disappointed.

ISBN: 978-1-897164-42-6

Complete EnglishSmart • Grade 8

B. Add quotation marks, dashes, or parentheses in the following sentences.

1. Samuel Langhorne Clemens 1835 – 1910 was a famous American humorist and writer better known by his pen name Mark Twain.

2. Twain is most noted for his novels The Adventures of Huckleberry Finn and The Adventures of Tom Sawyer among other works.

3. Mark Twain had a funny quotation: I have never taken any exercise except sleeping and resting.

4. Twain is often referred to as the father of American literature.

5. The word twain is an archaic term for two.

6. When Twain was four, his family moved to Hannibal, a port town on the Mississippi River the place which later inspired him to write The Adventures of Huckleberry Finn.

7. Advice for Little Girls 1867 was Twain's first published fiction.

8. Ernest Hemingway, another famous American writer, is best known for his novel The Old Man and the Sea.

9. Hemingway's style guide was: Use short sentences. Use short first paragraphs. Use vigorous English.

10. In 1920, Hemingway took a job at a newspaper in Toronto the *Toronto Star*.

11. Many critics touted Hemingway's A Clean, Well Lighted Place as one of the best stories ever written.

12. Hemingway once said: All modern American literature comes from one book by Mark Twain called Huckleberry Finn.

8 A Review on Punctuation

C. Some punctuation marks are missing or wrongly used in the following text. Add in the missing punctuation marks or correct the wrong ones.

Most plants are able to synthesize food (a process called photosynthesis) directly from inorganic compounds using light energy – for example, from the sun instead of eating other organisms, or relying on nutrients derived from them.

Plants absorb light primarily using the pigment chlorophyll which is why most plants are green in colour; although all cells in the green parts of a plant have chloroplasts most of the energy is captured in the leaves, the cells in the interior tissues of a leaf: called the mesophyll, contain about half a million chloroplasts for every square millimetre of leaf.

Do you know why chlorophyll looks green. Chlorophyll looks green, because it absorbs red and blue light making these colours unavailable to be seen by our eyes. It is the green light, which is not absorbed that finally reaches our eyes; making chlorophyll appear green.

The surface of the leaf is uniformly coated with a water-resistant waxy cuticle: to protect the leaf from excessive evaporation of water; it also decreases the absorption of ultraviolet light to reduce heating.

ISBN: 978-1-897164-42-6

D. Rewrite the following text in paragraphs and add in appropriate punctuation marks. Use capital letters wherever necessary.

christopher columbus 1451 – 1506 was an italian-born spanish explorer who sailed across the atlantic ocean in 1492 in the hope of finding a route to india mainly for spice trade he made four trips to the caribbean and south america between 1492 and 1504 on his first trip columbus led an expedition with three ships and about 90 crew members they set sail on august 3 1492 from palos spain on october 11 1492 they spotted the caribbean islands off southeastern north america columbus thought that he had made it to asia and called this area the indies and its inhabitants indians columbus also explored the northeast coast of cuba and the northern coast of hispaniola by december 5 there one of his ships ran aground and had to be abandoned he was received by the natives there who allowed columbus to leave some of his men behind columbus founded a settlement and left 39 of his men there then he headed for spain but another storm forced him into lisbon portugal after spending more than one week in lisbon he set sail for spain word of his finding the new world soon spread throughout europe

ISBN: 978-1-897164-42-6

Review 1

A. Fill in the blanks with the correct prepositions.

| up | at | to | from | into | with |

Wassily Kandinsky was a Russian painter and printmaker. As one of the most famous 20th-century artists, he is considered the first painter of modern abstract art. Prior to becoming an artist, Kandinsky had enrolled 1._____ the University of Moscow to study law and economics. Although he was quite successful in his studies, he gave 2._____ a promising teaching career and, at the age of 30, decided to settle in Munich to attend the Academy of Fine Arts. He went back 3._____ Moscow after the Russian Revolution in 1918, but finding himself in conflict with the official theories of art there, he returned 4._____ Germany. In his later years, Kandinsky moved 5._____ France, where he remained for the rest of his life.

Kandinsky drew inspiration 6._____ many sources during his youth in Moscow. He was fascinated by colour as a child. Although he seemed 7._____ have made no attempt to study art, his fascination with colour continued as he grew. In his early 20s, he travelled 8._____ the Vologda region north of Moscow, where the houses and churches were decorated with such shimmering colours that when he entered them, he felt he was moving 9._____ a painting. A

few years later, he even associated the act of painting 10._____ creating music, writing that "colour is the keyboard, the eyes are the hammer, the soul is the piano with the strings."

112

ISBN: 978-1-897164-42-6

B. Write "infinitive", "gerund", or "neither" for the underlined words.

1. Gabrielle went to the market <u>to buy</u> some fresh fruit and vegetables.

   _____

2. Eden used <u>coloured</u> chalk to draw an oak tree on the blackboard.

   _____

3. <u>To sing</u> well for the show, Matt needs to take care of his voice.

   _____

4. My brother loves everything from finding exotic ingredients to <u>cooking</u> wholesome meals.

   _____

5. Mr. Robinson found some <u>chopped</u> wood outside the house.

   _____

6. <u>To make</u> this dessert, all you need is your favourite yogurt and berries!

   _____

7. <u>Learning</u> how to dive is something that my sister has always wanted to do.

   _____

8. My little dog Jacob <u>looks</u> so forlorn sitting on the couch.

   _____

C. Rewrite these sentences so that the adjectives are in the correct order.

1. In my dream, I saw a red tiny house across the street.

   _____

2. The brown little porcupine in the cartoon will not stop poking her friend!

   _____

3. This museum houses a lot of Canadian beautiful furniture from the 1800s.

   _____

4. Jim wants to see if his grandmother still has her old, colourful soft quilt.

   _____

5. Jack is the name of my American, five-year-old cute cousin.

   _____

D. Fill in the blanks with the correct interrogative or relative adverbs.

The other day, my friend Dave asked me what my favourite dessert was. Without a doubt, I said, "It's crème brûlée!" He had no clue what it was, and asked me 1._____ I first had it. "At home, surprisingly," I replied. It was my brother who introduced me to this delicious treat (he was learning how to make it and asked me to do a taste test, at a time 2._____ I was ravenously hungry). "Well, what is crème brûlée, exactly?" Dave asked. I explained that it is a rich custard topped with a layer of hard caramel, made by burning sugar under the grill. "Very interesting," he said. "3._____ do you eat it?" I told him that I use a spoon to crack the caramel on top, and then slowly savour the rest. "Crème brûlée is actually one of the most popular desserts," I continued. Dave asked me 4._____ . "I don't exactly know," I said, "but the reason 5._____ I like it is the delightful contrast between the cold, creamy custard and the hard, hot layer of burnt sugar." He also asked me 6._____ this dessert originated. I told him that it is most likely France (since the name is in French), but my brother told me that some people believe its origin is in Spain, 7._____ it is called "crema catalana", and the custard base is aromatized with lemon and cinnamon.

E. Write the plural form of these compound words.

1.	seat belt	2.	farmhand
3.	panhandler	4.	passerby
5.	road map	6.	mailbox
7.	middle name	8.	close-up
9.	doggy bag	10.	high school
11.	police station	12.	guest of honour
13.	waffle cone	14.	brother-in-law

ISBN: 978-1-897164-42-6

F. Draw lines to match each pair of words with the correct meanings.

1. advise   •   •   opinion about what should be done

   advice   •   •   give someone advice

2. site   •   •   place used for an activity, a building, or a town

   sight   •   •   act of seeing; spectacle

3. alter   •   •   table or stone for offering to a god

   altar   •   •   modify the style or size of something

4. affect   •   •   result or consequence of an action

   effect   •   •   touch the feelings of someone; influence

5. counsel   •   •   formally given advice; consultation

   consul   •   •   person appointed by a country to live in a foreign city to foster understanding and promote trade

G. Write sentences to show the difference in meaning between each pair of words.

1. among   between

_____

_____

2. lay   lie

_____

_____

3. stationary   stationery

_____

_____

ISBN: 978-1-897164-42-6

H. Complete these sentences with coordinating or correlative conjunctions.

and	but	yet	or	for

either...or	neither...nor	not only...but also

1. Time is running out! We have to put the finishing touches on our lobster salad _____ we would be out of this cooking contest.

2. This cup of cappuccino is bitter _____ comforting, not to mention light _____ frothy!

3. Dr. Summer's project on the genetics of hyper behaviour will take years to complete, _____ anything that requires careful study is time-consuming.

4. "I'd better catch up with that rabbit _____ I'll miss the important message _____ miss the entire dinner party!" Becky was saying this to herself in her dream last night.

5. _____ Mom _____ Dad knows how to make chicken Kiev, a very yummy dish. Only my brother does!

6. Mrs. Stephanoff lets us choose _____ Monday _____ Tuesday for our French test.

7. Carrie wants to visit me in Whitby _____ she has no idea when she could come _____ what bus to take.

8. As Coach Simon says, _____ Tom _____ Dave will make a very good team captain this year. We are very lucky.

9. There is _____ a good book _____ a good TV show to help me get through this long afternoon, which is great!

10. Kevin knows how to take care of turtles _____ not frogs _____ he suggests that I seek help from his buddy Paul.

ISBN: 978-1-897164-42-6

I. Add the correct punctuation marks in the following.

Iceland can be a challenging country for engineers, not because of the frozen barrens steam hissing from geothermal vents bizarrely shaped lava rocks or even volcanoes spouting fire. It is challenging because of the spirit folk lurking in the land.

Though Iceland is the most geographically remote of all European countries being a tiny island just below the Arctic Circle it is technologically advanced and highly literate the literacy rate is 100 per cent! Yet Icelanders are also pretty serious about other-worldly beings, like gnomes trolls elves lovelings light-fairies sisters to Tinkerbell and a unique species called huldufolk, or hidden people. More than half of all Icelanders believe they may really exist. As noted by Arni Bjornsson, who is the head of ethnological studies at the National Museum of Iceland Even hard-headed engineers, who say they don't hold with superstition, will build a road around a certain hill or boulder rather than take the risk of offending elves. In fact highway engineers in recent years have been forced to reroute roads around supposed elf dwellings.

So, why do Icelanders believe that they share their abode with tiny and hidden creatures? Here is one theory from Olafur Ragnar Grimsson, the country's president it is because of Icelanders' abiding sense of loneliness and isolation. Icelanders are few in number he explains so they double their population with tales of elves and fairies. Of course this doesn't seem to make sense, but as Arni Bjornsson says It is hard to be totally scientific in a country as spectacularly strange as ours.

ISBN: 978-1-897164-42-6

9 Phrases

A **phrase** is a group of related words that does not include a verb.

Examples: Noun phrase: *the tall and strong player*
Participial phrase: *the road <u>leading to the church</u>*
Infinitive phrase: *the first runner <u>to reach the finish line</u>*
Prepositional phrase: *the house <u>by the river</u>*

Noun Phrases

A **noun phrase** is made up of all the words that are about the noun itself so that together, they form a unit of thought. Sometimes a noun phrase is broken up, with part of the noun phrase delayed until the end of the sentence.

Examples: <u>Two projects on making efficient use of solar energy</u> have been completed.
(noun phrase; as subject of the sentence)

<u>Two projects</u> have been completed <u>on making efficient use of solar energy</u>.
(broken up noun phrase)

Note that noun phrases can be formed with participial phrases, infinitive phrases, or prepositional phrases.

A. Underline the noun phrases in the following sentences.

1. If you look carefully, you'll see several small stars within the big star.

2. The police are investigating an accident involving a stolen truck.

3. The unexpected heavy snowstorm paralyzed traffic.

4. Everyone in Mrs. Templeton's class was given a goodie bag.

5. Several men were spotted swimming towards the lighthouse.

6. The volunteers to help organize the event are having a meeting.

7. His office is in that building across the street.

8. The coach asked those failing to complete three laps to continue their practice.

9. When he turned around, he saw a man standing right behind him.

10. All the players of the opposing team stayed behind for a photoshoot.

ISBN: 978-1-897164-42-6

B. Using noun phrases, turn the following pairs of sentences or complex sentences into simple sentences.

1. We spent our weekend in a houseboat. The houseboat was well-equipped.

   _____

2. On his way to school, he came across a dog. There was a backpack on its back.

   _____

3. Anyone who wants to join the team will have to undergo a selection process this weekend.

   _____

4. The package costs $60. It includes all the accessories.

   _____

5. Those who fail to comply with the rules will be penalized.

   _____

6. The pitcher missed the strike zone time and again. He was exhausted.

   _____

7. The documentary lasts almost two hours. It features an hour-long interview with various environmentalists.

   _____

8. The town has a population of about 1000. It is between Meadowville and Bloomsfield.

   _____

9. The team had a celebration at the stadium. It was attended by more than 10 000 fans.

   _____

10. Simon picked up a bottle. There was a message in it.

    _____

    _____

    _____

Appositive Phrases

An appositive is the re-naming of a word that immediately precedes it. An **appositive phrase**, therefore, is used to provide more information about the noun or noun phrase that precedes it.

Examples: The starting pitcher, <u>a rookie with an ERA of 4.05</u>, is poised to win his tenth game of the season. *(noun phrase as appositive)*

His favourite exercise, <u>jogging in the morning</u>, helps keep him in good shape. *(gerund phrase as appositive)*

My ultimate goal – <u>to win the championship</u> – looks more and more within reach. *(infinitive phrase as appositive)*

C. Add appositive phrases to the following sentences.

1. My uncle teaches me a lot about planets and stars.

   _____

2. We hope to win this decisive game.

   _____

3. He was bothered by the dilemma.

   _____

4. The new receptionist is both courteous and efficient.

   _____

5. The journey soon turned out to be a nightmare.

   _____

6. They finally decided to drop the plan.

   _____

7. The contestant remained strong after seven rounds of competition.

   _____

8. Mary suggested having the party at a banquet hall.

   _____

ISBN: 978-1-897164-42-6

D. Read the following text about sharks. Rewrite the underlined sentences by using phrases.

1. <u>Sharks have a keen sense of smell, and some species are able to detect as little as one part per million of blood in seawater!</u> Apart from relying on their superior sense of smell to find prey, they also use the lateral lines running along their sides to sense movement in the water when the prey is at a close range. The special sensory pores on their heads also enable them to detect electrical fields created by prey.

2. <u>Sharks' eyes are well adapted to the marine environment because they have a tissue called tapetum lucidum.</u> This tissue is behind the retina. It helps reflect light back to the retina and increase visibility in the dark waters.

Although sharks have eyelids, they do not blink. To protect their eyes, some sharks have nictitating membranes. These membranes cover the eyes during predation, and when the shark is being attacked. 3. <u>However, some species do not have these membranes and they roll their eyes backwards to protect them when they strike their prey.</u> The Great White Shark is one of such species.

1. _____

_____

_____

_____

2. _____

_____

_____

_____

3. _____

_____

_____

_____

ISBN: 978-1-897164-42-6

10 Voice and Mood

Active and Passive Voices

Verbs in the **active voice** show the action of the subject. Verbs in the **passive voice** show something else acting on the subject. While the active voice is more forceful and should be used whenever possible, the passive voice provides a shift of emphasis – from the doer to the thing or person being acted upon.

Examples: *We ate ten pizzas!* *(active)*

Ten pizzas were eaten by us! *(passive, with emphasis on the ten pizzas we ate)*

Note that in using the passive voice, we sometimes leave out the "doer" so that the reader's attention is further directed at the person or thing being acted upon.

Example: *Ten pizzas were eaten!*

A. Read the following text and underline the parts of the sentences where the passive voice is used.

Dodge ball is a fun game enjoyed by grade school children. There are many ways of playing it. A popular way is to divide the players into two teams. The players on one team stay inside a circle and those on the other team stand around outside. A big, rubber ball is used and thrown at the players inside the circle. The players inside may run around whenever they want to dodge the ball as long as they stay within the circle. The ball can only be thrown to hit the players below the waist. If the ball is thrown and hits someone above the waist, the thrower has to leave the game. If a player in the circle is hit, he or she becomes one of the players outside the circle. The game is over when only one person remains inside the circle.

ISBN: 978-1-897164-42-6

B. **Change the passive voice in (A) into active voice. Make any other necessary changes.**

_____

_____

_____

_____

_____

_____

C. **Rewrite the following sentences using the passive voice. You may leave out the "doer" if you feel that it does not affect the clarity of the sentence.**

1. The firefighters put out the fire in less than an hour.

_____

2. We will hold the annual meeting as scheduled.

_____

3. The teacher handed out the pamphlets to all the Grade 8 students.

_____

4. We should return all borrowed books to the library before noon today.

_____

5. They saw a baby whale about a mile off the shore.

_____

6. The principal awarded Janet The Best Student of the Year Award.

_____

7. Strangely, they never approached us.

_____

8. They considered the show one of the best they had ever seen.

_____

ISBN: 978-1-897164-42-6

10 Voice and Mood

Mood

There are three types of **mood**: indicative, imperative, and subjunctive.

Most verbs we use are in the **indicative mood**, that is, to indicate something.

Example: *The teacher will announce the test results soon.*

Some verbs are in the **imperative mood**, which expresses commands or requests.

Example: *Please let me know by noon today.*

When verbs are used to express wishes or something that is not true, they are in the **subjunctive mood**.

Examples: *If she had told my teacher (but she didn't), I would have been in great trouble (I wasn't in great trouble).*

I wish I could have a million dollars (I don't have a million dollars).

Note the use of past or past perfect tense to denote something that is a wish or not true.

D. **Read the following sentences and indicate the types of mood: indicative (IND), imperative (IMP), and subjunctive (SUB).**

1. They are still awaiting the medical report. _____

2. Ms. Lyman was there to make sure that everything was in order. _____

3. If he were our coach, we could be in for more trouble. _____

4. They wished they had not done it. _____

5. I hope to be able to finish my writing by tomorrow. _____

6. Tell Susan that her mother called her just now. _____

7. You should go and seek advice from Mr. Walton. _____

8. Frank wouldn't have been injured if he had been more careful. _____

9. Make sure that each of them is given a bonus pack. _____

10. We can tell if Keith is lying by looking at his posture. _____

11. If I were given the task, I would complete it on time. _____

12. Don't assume that you can do whatever you like. _____

ISBN: 978-1-897164-42-6

E. Change the mood in the following sentences to imperative.

1. I wonder if you could let me have it as soon as possible.

   _____

2. You must not waste any more time on the minor details.

   _____

3. I would appreciate it if you could contact Mrs. Jones on my behalf.

   _____

4. You may choose to buy it online if you want to save time.

   _____

5. You should bear right and turn left when you see the sign "Snowview".

   _____

   _____

F. Complete the following sentences using the subjunctive mood.

1. The sisters wished _____

   _____

2. If there was a hurricane, _____

   _____

3. They wouldn't have won the game _____

   _____

4. How I wish I _____

   _____

5. Had we not received Eugene's help, _____

   _____

6. If we all stayed together, _____

   _____

ISBN: 978-1-897164-42-6

11 More on the Passive Voice

The passive voice provides a shift of emphasis – from the doer to the thing or person being acted upon. However, we should not overuse it. Note that the tense of the verb in the passive voice should be the same as that in the active voice.

Below is a chart showing the tenses and verb forms in the passive voice.

Tense/Verb Form	Active Voice	Passive Voice
Simple present	does	is done
Present continuous	is doing	is being done
Present infinitive	to do	to be done
Future	will do	will be done
Simple past	did	was done
Past continuous	was doing	was being done
Present perfect	has done	has been done
Past perfect	had done	had been done
Conditional present	would do	would be done
Conditional past	would have done	would have been done
Perfect infinitive	to have done	to have been done
Present participle/gerund	doing	being done
Perfect participle	having done	having been done

A. Rewrite the sentences if the verb form is wrong.

1. Can you tell me where the party held?

_____

2. The witness was being interviewed by the police officer.

_____

3. They did not know if the matter had settled.

_____

4. We are giving a second chance to do the experiment. The findings have to be submitted by Wednesday.

_____

ISBN: 978-1-897164-42-6

5. It is too early to tell whether or not he would be selected to the team.

_____

6. An announcement will be made as soon as we receive more details.

_____

B. Change the following sentences into the passive voice.

1. They will launch the space shuttle after they have fixed the problem.

_____

_____

2. I would have solved the problem if you had given me the formula.

_____

_____

3. The refugees needed food and shelter desperately.

_____

4. We have to redo the project as the teacher considers it too sketchy.

_____

5. The storm woke me up in the wee hours of the morning.

_____

6. They allowed no one to enter the premises without authorization.

_____

7. The robber had shot the woman twice before the police gunned him down.

_____

8. If Mrs. Marshall postponed the deadline, we would finish the project in time.

_____

ISBN: 978-1-897164-42-6

11 More on the Passive Voice

Passive Form Using "Get/Have Something Done"

In using "**get/have something done**" to convey passive voice, we describe situations where we want someone else to do something for us. We focus on the result of the activity rather than the person or object that performs the activity.

Example: *He wanted someone <u>to repair his car</u>. (active)*

He wanted <u>to have his car repaired</u>. (passive)

C. Change the following sentences into the passive voice.

1. Mr. Shaffer renovated his bathroom.

   _____

2. We completed the assignment before the deadline.

   _____

3. She thinks she can finish filling out all the forms in an hour.

   _____

4. He wants someone to fix the broken windows.

   _____

Passive Form Using "Need + __ing"

This construction, like "get/have something done", conveys a passive meaning. By using this structure, we focus on the person or thing that will experience the action.

D. Rewrite the following sentences using "need + __ing".

1. Our school is run-down and it needs to be renovated.

   _____

2. He did not realize that the food needed to be reheated.

   _____

ISBN: 978-1-897164-42-6

3. The floor was so dirty that it needed to be scrubbed.

    _____

4. The wild horse needs to be tamed before anyone can ride it.

    _____

E. **Read the following text about Wayne Gretzky and underline the sentences which you feel can be written in the passive voice. Then write them in the space provided.**

The Official Encyclopedia of the NHL describes Gretzky as "the greatest player of all time". Many sportswriters, coaches, and fans have also called him "the greatest hockey player ever". Along with his many awards and achievements, Gretzky is the only player to ever have his playing number, 99, officially retired across the entire National Hockey League. He is generally regarded as the best player of his era.

Despite his talent, Gretzky spent at least four hours a day practising hockey. People attributed Gretzky's dominance throughout his career to the amount of time he put into his practice. Of course, we should not neglect the fact that he was a natural prodigy. At 16, Gretzky's skills were already described as "a magic touch". He moved the puck well and he managed to play both offence and defence. He was a player that any team could build their hockey club around. People often described him as someone who "seems to have eyes in the back of his head".

_____

_____

_____

_____

_____

_____

ISBN: 978-1-897164-42-6

12 A Review on Sentences

Types of Sentences by Structure

Simple sentence: consists of a single independent clause with no dependent clauses.

Compound sentence: consists of two or more independent clauses with no dependent clauses. These clauses are joined together using conjunctions, punctuation, or both.

Complex sentence: consists of one independent clause with at least one dependent clause.

Compound-complex sentence: consists of two or more independent clauses, one of which has at least one dependent clause.

A. Rewrite the following groups of sentences.

1. They finally reached the destination. The other teams were already there.

   Compound sentence: _____

   _____

   Complex sentence: _____

   _____

2. The oil tank started leaking. Our car could stop any minute. We would be forced to walk our way across the deserted plain.

   Compound sentence: _____

   _____

   Compound-complex sentence: _____

   _____

3. Although we searched everywhere, we were unable to find the key. Without the key, there was no way we could enter the house.

   Simple sentences: _____

   _____

   Compound-complex sentence: _____

   _____

ISBN: 978-1-897164-42-6

B. Try rewriting the following text by using more compound, complex, and compound-complex sentences in place of simple sentences.

Bats can fly but they are not birds. In fact they are mammals. Bats' forelimbs are developed into wings. Their wing-like forelimbs make them the only flying mammal in the world. Flying squirrels do not actually fly. They can only glide for a short distance.

There are about 1100 species of bats worldwide. About 70% of bats are insectivores. They eat insects. Of the remainder, most feed on fruits and juices.
Three species of bats live on blood and little animals. Bats do not have good vision. They rely on echolocation to find food. Echolocation is the ability to emit high-pitched sounds. They are able to locate objects by listening to the echoes.

Some smaller bat species are important pollinators of tropical flowers. They also help spread seeds by eating fruits. One species of bats has the longest tongue of any mammal. They can reach deep down into the long cup shape of some flowers with their long tongue. When their tongue retracts, it coils up inside their rib cage.

_____

_____

_____

_____

_____

_____

_____

_____

_____

_____

_____

ISBN: 978-1-897164-42-6

12 A Review on Sentences

Types of Sentences by Purpose

Sentences can also be classified based on their purpose.

Declarative sentence: makes a statement
Interrogative sentence: requests information
Exclamatory sentence: shows surprises and strong feelings
Imperative sentence: makes a demand or gives a command

C. Rewrite the following sentences.

1. The firework displays are really spectacular.

    Exclamatory: _____

2. I think you should submit by Friday or else you'll be penalized.

    Imperative: _____

3. "How disrespectful John was!" said Mrs. Carter.

    Declarative: _____

4. I'd like to know why he didn't tell his mother about it.

    Interrogative: _____

5. They asked if the guests would stay overnight.

    Interrogative: _____

6. Patrick asked, "Has Simon been to Prince Edward Island before?"

    Declarative: _____

7. "What a splendid evening this is!" said Teresa.

    Declarative: _____

8. I want to know if there is any other course of action to take.

    Interrogative: _____

9. The man warned the child to watch out for the car.

    Exclamatory: _____

ISBN: 978-1-897164-42-6

Major and Minor Sentences

A **major sentence** is a regular sentence; it has a subject and a predicate. A **minor sentence**, on the other hand, is an irregular sentence. It may not follow grammatical rules. Headings, formulaic expressions, proverbs, etc. are minor sentences.

Examples: *I saw Adrienne yesterday when I was on my way home.* (major)
Wow! (minor)

D. Give an example for each type of sentence stated below.

1. A compound sentence

   _____

2. A compound-complex sentence

   _____

3. An exclamatory sentence

   _____

4. A proverb that is a minor sentence

   _____

5. An interrogative sentence

   _____

6. An imperative sentence

   _____

7. A heading that is a minor sentence

   _____

8. A major sentence that is a simple sentence

   _____

9. A complex sentence

   _____

10. A declarative sentence

    _____

ISBN: 978-1-897164-42-6

13 Dependent Clauses as Nouns, Adjectives, and Adverbs

Dependent Clauses

A **dependent clause** is a clause that cannot stand alone as a sentence. It has to attach to another clause and its function is to add more information to that other clause.

Examples: *He arrived at the reception. (sentence; meaning complete)*

When he arrived at the reception (dependent clause; meaning not complete)

When he arrived at the reception, he saw his former teacher, Mrs. Keith. (add more information to the main clause)

A. Convert the following sentences into dependent clauses and use them to make complex sentences.

1. She missed the 8:30 a.m. train.

   _____

2. They sped past an old building.

   _____

3. Mrs. Wyle did not recognize him.

   _____

4. It was past midnight.

   _____

5. The road was slippery.

   _____

6. We all cheered for him.

   _____

7. The farm stretched far and wide.

   _____

8. There wasn't anyone in the room.

   _____

ISBN: 978-1-897164-42-6

Dependent Clauses as Nouns

Like a noun, a **noun clause** acts as the subject or object of a verb or the object of a preposition. It answers questions like "who(m)?" or "what?".

Examples: I think <u>that Lucy is reliable</u>. *(What do you think?)*

<u>Where the robbers are hiding</u> is unknown. *(What is unknown?)*

B. Underline the noun clauses in the following sentences.

1. He realized that he needed to seek Mr. Jenkin's permission before going ahead with the scheme.

2. Whatever you do has to be both sensible and meaningful.

3. The fans were hopeful that their team could score in the last 60 seconds.

4. Whether or not they could make it remains to be seen.

5. They did not know which train passed by the little border town.

C. Convert the underlined part in each of the following sentences into a noun clause. Make any other necessary changes.

1. <u>They</u> will be punished.

   _____

2. We were excited <u>about something</u>.

   _____

3. No one was certain <u>about it</u>.

   _____

4. The police did not notice <u>an important clue</u>.

   _____

   _____

5. <u>Someone</u> will get the prize.

   _____

   _____

ISBN: 978-1-897164-42-6

13 Dependent Clauses as Nouns, Adjectives, and Adverbs

Dependent Clauses as Adjectives

Like an adjective, an **adjective clause** modifies a noun or a pronoun, answering questions like "which?" or "what kind of?".

Example: *Jenny loved the bag <u>that her mom gave her for her birthday</u>. (Which bag?)*

In formal writing, an adjective clause begins with a relative pronoun such as "who", "that", or "which". In informal writing or speech, we often leave out the relative pronoun.

Example: *The man whom I met this morning is Sam's uncle. (formal)*

The man I met this morning is Sam's uncle. (informal)

D. Expand each of the following sentences by adding an adjective clause.

1. The house looked somewhat run-down.

   _____

2. He showed the plan.

   _____

3. The seafood dinner was delicious.

   _____

4. Jeff was looking for the book.

   _____

5. Have you seen the painting?

   _____

6. He claimed the prize.

   _____

7. No one noticed the little boy.

   _____

8. Were there any signs?

   _____

ISBN: 978-1-897164-42-6

Dependent Clauses as Adverbs

An **adverb clause** takes the place of an adverb in the main clause. It answers questions such as "when?", "where?", "why?", and "how?".

Example: *He built a house <u>where the old church used to stand</u>. (Where?)*

We usually begin an adverb clause with a subordinating conjunction like "because", "when", "where", "since", "after", or "so that".

E. **Complete the following sentences with adverb clauses.**

1. When _____ ,
   the plane had already taken off.

2. Since _____ ,
   we can hold the game this Sunday.

3. They turned down the volume so that _____

   _____

4. The mayor decided to plant a tree where _____

   _____

5. The Watsons did not go on the trip because _____

   _____

F. **Identify the underlined clauses. Write "N" for noun clauses, "ADJ" for adjective clauses, and "ADV" for adverb clauses.**

1. He put a mark <u>where he thought the treasure was buried</u>. _____

2. <u>Wherever you go</u> is none of my concern. _____

3. The place <u>where we went for a picnic last Saturday</u> is beautiful. _____

4. Do you know that the player <u>who scored the winning run</u> is my brother? _____

5. I don't believe <u>that he knew the code</u>. _____

6. It was too late <u>when the paramedics arrived</u>. _____

ISBN: 978-1-897164-42-6

14 Report Structures

To report what someone said, we usually use our own words rather than repeating their exact words.

Examples: *John said, "I don't want to go to the party."*

John said that <u>he didn't</u> want to go to the party.

Or *John said he didn't want to go to the party.*

John asked, "Do you want to go to the party?"

John asked <u>if I wanted</u> to go to the party.

John said to me, "Wait until Matt arrives."

John <u>told me to wait</u> until Matt arrived.

A. Change the following statements into the report structure.

1. Jen's mother said to her, "Take the pup for a walk."

   _____

2. Linda asked Sean, "Do you want some more coffee?"

   _____

3. Our teacher said to us, "The practice will start at 7:00 p.m. sharp."

   _____

   _____

4. "I don't know who you're referring to," replied Mavis indifferently.

   _____

   _____

5. The coach asked him, "Have you ever tried the diving catch?"

   _____

   _____

6. "We may not be able to reach there before midnight," said the guide to the worried tourists.

   _____

   _____

ISBN: 978-1-897164-42-6

Verbs Showing Thoughts and Feelings

In reporting what others say, we may use verbs to reflect their thoughts and feelings.

Example: Beatrice said, "I'm wrong."

Beatrice <u>felt</u> that she was wrong.

Or   Beatrice <u>admitted</u> that she was wrong.

Verbs to show thoughts and feelings

mention   explain   complain   admit   claim   order
agree   insist   decide   promise   warn
remind   reassure   persuade   convince   suggest

B. **Replace each of the underlined verbs with one that conveys thoughts and feelings. Write the new verb above the underlined one.**

1. The doctor <u>said</u> that I had to apply the ointment every day.

2. They <u>said</u> that they would forge ahead even without our support.

3. Pamela <u>said</u> that she would never do that again.

4. The teacher <u>told</u> us to submit our project no later than Thursday.

5. He <u>said</u> that he had not done it.

6. She <u>said</u> that her plan was the most cost-effective.

7. We <u>said</u> that we would hold a meeting to discuss the matter further.

8. The policeman <u>told</u> him to drop the knife.

ISBN: 978-1-897164-42-6

C. Read each group of sentences and decide what was actually said.

Example: Mrs. Wiley reminded the class not to cheat. She warned that she would disqualify anyone found cheating. She added that she would report any case of cheating to the principal.

Mrs. Wiley said to her class, "Remember not to cheat. Anyone found cheating would be disqualified, and I'd report it to the principal."

1. The coach was furious and demanded that the players practise for another two hours. Based on their performance, he didn't think they had a chance of winning the game.

   _____

   _____

   _____

   _____

2. When he saw the manager, he explained that he was new and didn't know the rules. He asked her for another chance and he promised that he would not do that again.

   _____

   _____

   _____

   _____

3. When the party was over, Mariam thanked Dave for the wonderful evening. Dave felt that he had a wonderful time with her too, and he wondered if he could pay her a visit sometime the following week.

   _____

   _____

   _____

   _____

ISBN: 978-1-897164-42-6

D. Transform the following into the report structure. Add connecting sentences whenever you feel necessary.

"I've no idea why Ben thinks it that way," said Terry.

"What way?" asked Heather.

"That we gang up on him."

"Well, do you?"

"Well, not really; he simply isolates himself."

"But you must've done something that made him think that you're ganging up on him."

"Maybe."

"Why don't you invite him to our gathering?"

"I don't think he'll come."

"How would you know if you don't try?"

"All right, I'll give it a try."

_____

_____

_____

_____

_____

_____

_____

_____

_____

_____

_____

ISBN: 978-1-897164-42-6

15 Conditional Clauses (1)

Conditional Clauses

We use clauses with "**if**" to talk about a possible situation and its results. The conditional clause can come before or after the main clause.

Examples: *If the weather is fine, we will go fishing.*

We will go fishing if the weather is fine.

Note the use of a comma when the conditional clause comes before the main clause.

For something that is generally true or happens often, we use the present or present perfect tense in both the main and the conditional clauses.

Example: *If the dog <u>barks</u>, it probably <u>senses</u> something unusual.*

Sometimes an imperative in the main clause can be used.

Example: *Let me know if you don't receive the dispatch by noon.*

A. **Complete the following conditional sentences that are telling something that is generally true or happens often.**

1. If it's Sunday, _____

2. Wake me up _____

3. If he has given it to you, _____

4. Don't expect them to arrive early _____

5. Lock all the doors and windows _____

6. If they strike, _____

7. If they agree, _____

8. Tell her not to go _____

9. If we count by 10's, _____

10. No one notices us _____

ISBN: 978-1-897164-42-6

When we are talking about something that may happen in the future, we use the present or present perfect tense in the conditional clause and the simple future in the main clause.

Example: If it <u>rains</u>, we <u>will cancel</u> the game.

B. Complete the following conditional sentences with the correct form of the verbs given.

1. If Cecilia is willing to go the extra mile, she

   _____ (stand) a good chance of landing the job.

2. I _____ (make) good use of it if you give it to me.

3. No one _____ (find) out if you keep it a secret.

4. If we both agree to go ahead immediately, we _____ (be) able to complete it on schedule.

5. If you _____ (travel) to China, you will need to apply for a visa.

When we are talking about something that is unlikely to happen, we use the past tense in the conditional clause and "would" in the main clause. Note that "were" is used instead of "was" in the conditional clause.

Example: If he were the chairman, he would cast the decisive vote.

C. Complete the following conditional sentences that talk about something unlikely to happen.

1. If we were denied entry, _____

2. They would invite you _____

3. If I were the teacher, _____

4. If Devon came, _____

5. The team would not play _____

ISBN: 978-1-897164-42-6

15 Conditional Clauses (1)

When we are talking about something that could have happened in the past but did not actually happen, we use the past perfect tense in the conditional clause and "would have" and a past participle in the main clause.

Example: If I <u>had known</u> about it, I <u>would have told</u> you.

  (Fact: I did not know about it and so I did not tell you.)

D. Complete the following conditional sentences with the correct form of the verbs given.

1. The team would have lost if Derek _____ (not hit) a homerun in the ninth inning.

2. If you _____ (be) more supportive, we _____ (be) able to make it.

3. They _____ (survive) if there _____ (be) more provisions on board.

4. We _____ (stop) if he _____ (warn) us.

5. If the visibility _____ (be) better, the multi-vehicle accident

    _____ (not occur).

6. If Stephen _____ (keep) his cool, he _____ (not be punished).

7. She _____ (win) if she _____ (not miss) the last shot.

8. If the gate _____ (be locked), the animals

    _____ (not run) away.

ISBN: 978-1-897164-42-6

E. Read the following sentences. Check the correct sentences and rewrite the wrong ones on the lines provided.

1. If Josh gets hold of the information, he will make it available to all of us. ☐

_____

2. I will be a multi-millionaire if I won the lottery. ☐

_____

3. If he tried just a little harder, he would have passed the test. ☐

_____

4. They would not have succeeded if you don't help them. ☐

_____

5. We will wait for him if he had called. ☐

_____

6. If he recognized you, he would give you a ride. ☐

_____

7. You would not be charged if you showed them the pass. ☐

_____

8. The outcome would have been totally different if he didn't make the wrong decision. ☐

_____

9. Don't reveal it even if they asked you. ☐

_____

10. If we are given two choices, the chance of picking the right one will be higher. ☐

_____

11. If the car hadn't swerved in front of me, I wouldn't have driven onto the walkway. ☐

_____

ISBN: 978-1-897164-42-6

16 Conditional Clauses (2)

Use of Modals

Sometimes we use **modals** like "can", "may", and "must" in conditional clauses, and in the main clauses, we can use the present tense for something that happens often, "will" for likely events in the future, "would" for unlikely events, and "would have" for possible events that never happened. Modals can also be used in main clauses.

Examples: *They <u>could</u> join us if they wanted to.*

Meet me at the entrance if you <u>can</u> make it.

A. Complete the following conditional sentences that involve the use of modals.

1. If you can't swim, _____

2. If you must see him today, _____

3. They might not go ahead _____

4. She might want to get a copy _____

   _____

5. They may make special arrangements _____

   _____

6. If he should ever question your integrity, _____

   _____

7. The teacher reminds us that if we can't attend the ceremony, _____

   _____

8. The speaker could take a few more

   questions _____

   _____

   _____

   _____

ISBN: 978-1-897164-42-6

Omitting "If"

When "had", "were", or "should" is used in a conditional clause, we may omit "if" and begin the sentence with it, followed by the subject.

Example: *If the committee should reconsider the matter, I would be willing to explain further.*

Should the committee reconsider the matter, I would be willing to explain further.

B. Rewrite the following conditional sentences in another way.

1. If they had told me about it, I would not have made such a remark.

   _____

2. If I were elected president, I would make you the treasurer.

   _____

3. They wouldn't have made the trip if they had read the news.

   _____

4. If he had teamed up with me, we would have won the tournament.

   _____

5. If they should appear, I would sneak out by the backdoor.

   _____

6. They would be held responsible if they were at the scene.

   _____

7. They couldn't have beaten us if we had stayed focused.

   _____

8. If the teacher had announced it in advance, there wouldn't have been so much anxiety.

   _____

   _____

ISBN: 978-1-897164-42-6

16 Conditional Clauses (2)

Other Beginning Words for Conditional Clauses

Other than "if", we can use other words to begin conditional clauses to indicate that one event only happens or is true if another event happens or is true.

Some of the common expressions are: provided that, only if, unless, even if, so long as, as long as.

C. **Complete the following conditional sentences with suitable expressions.**

1. He won't do it _____ you tell him to. He only listens to you.

2. _____ we start right away, we won't be able to meet the deadline because there is much more work than we first expected.

3. The ice cubes won't melt _____ you keep them in the freezer.

4. _____ we keep quiet, no one will notice that we are here.

5. I won't believe it _____ I see it with my own eyes.

6. We shouldn't pass judgement on him too soon, _____ he looks suspicious.

7. She says she will join us _____ Kitty doesn't come. They simply can't get along with each other.

8. They are willing to help you _____ you don't hold back any vital information.

9. Pansy wouldn't give in _____ we offered her some favourable terms.

10. _____ you can come earlier, you won't be able to meet up with him.

ISBN: 978-1-897164-42-6

D. Read the following sentences. Check the correct sentences and rewrite the wrong ones on the lines provided.

1. If they remain quiet for the rest of the lesson, the teacher will make them stay behind.

   _____

2. Had he not shouted for help, no one would have noticed him in the dark.

   _____

3. As long as you didn't say a word, I will leave the matter behind.

   _____

4. They would go ahead unless you tell them not to.

   _____

5. The show would be held as planned, provided that the venue is confirmed.

   _____

6. Were he not careful, he would have fallen into the water and drowned.

   _____

7. She might agree if you ask politely.

   _____

8. Only if you sign the document, they wouldn't have approved the funding.

   _____

9. Should you come tonight, you would be able to meet Charles and his cousin.

   _____

10. If your mother discovered it, you would have been in trouble.

   _____

ISBN: 978-1-897164-42-6

A. Write "noun", "appositive", or "neither" above the underlined phrases.

Musical theatre is <u>a form of theatre involving music, songs, spoken dialogue, and dance</u>. Combined with visual aspects such as lighting and set design, these elements work as an integrated whole to make the story, <u>with all its humour, sadness, love, and anger</u>, come amazingly alive.

Musical theatre works, <u>commonly called "musicals"</u>, are performed everywhere from <u>big-budget venues in London and New York City</u> to smaller performance spaces like schools. Some productions also go on tour, <u>hopping from city to city</u>. In addition to Britain and the United States, <u>the hubs of performing arts</u>, vibrant musical theatre scenes can be found in Canada, Germany, Austria, France, Japan, Australia, and many other countries.

Les Misérables, Cats, The Phantom of the Opera, West Side Story, and *The Fantasticks* are well-known musicals. Interestingly, *The Fantasticks,* <u>a musical made on a very low budget</u> (because the creators could only spend $900 on the set and $541 on costumes), ended up being <u>the longest-running musical in history</u>. The show closed on January 13, 2002 after an astounding 17 162 performances!

ISBN: 978-1-897164-42-6

B. Circle the correct mood of each sentence. Then write another sentence of the same mood.

1. Roma tomatoes are good in salads because they are very sweet and meaty.

    _____

    _____

indicative
subjunctive

2. Sara wishes that she had not left the house so early.

    _____

    _____

imperative
subjunctive

3. Pick up a carton of milk and some yogurt on your way home.

    _____

    _____

imperative
indicative

4. If the builders had done everything properly, the Leaning Tower of Pisa might not be as famous as it is.

    _____

    _____

subjunctive
indicative

5. "Homer" is actually the name of a Greek poet from many, many years ago.

    _____

    _____

subjunctive
indicative

6. I hope to finish making this salad before my friends arrive.

    _____

    _____

indicative
subjunctive

7. Parmesan is a kind of cheese originally made at Parma, a province in Italy.

    _____

    _____

subjunctive
indicative

ISBN: 978-1-897164-42-6

C. Rewrite each sentence by focusing on the person or thing being acted on.

1. The girls performed an Egyptian dance in Act One.

   _____

2. Michael led the procession of animals across the stage.

   _____

3. The majestic march wrapped up the never-ending Act Two.

   _____

4. Andrea accidentally made a hole in her bulky costume.

   _____

5. The elephant sniffed Lola's shoulder when it came near.

   _____

6. We should treat everything we do as though it were a dress rehearsal.

   _____

7. The audience appreciated the Egyptian dance and the excellent singing.

   _____

   _____

8. The stagehand raised the curtain again for the cast to take a final bow.

   _____

   _____

D. Change the following into the passive voice by using "need + __ing".

1. To make it look seamless, every detail needed to be rehearsed.

   _____

2. Some soloists needed to be reassured to perform their best.

   _____

3. The costumes needed to be cleaned after each production.

   _____

ISBN: 978-1-897164-42-6

E. **Identify the shaded sentences. Write "declarative", "interrogative", "exclamatory", "imperative", "compound", or "conditional". Use each answer only once.**

Have you ever heard of the International Save the Children Alliance? **1.** It is a worldwide non-profitable organization dedicated to improving the lives of children, with operations in over 115 countries including Britain, the United States, Mexico, and Canada.

If you live in Canada, you can become involved with **2.** Save the Children Canada, which helps children affected by HIV/AIDS, exploitation and abuse, and conflict and disaster. It also ensures their rights and helps provide basic education. The charity works **3.** not only in Canada but also reaches out to help children in Central America, the Caribbean, South America, West Africa, East Africa, the Middle East, and South Asia.

There are many ways to get involved: from raising **4.** funds through a bake sale to organizing a community group that raises awareness. Not only will you deepen your skills and broaden your personal horizons, you will also be making small steps that can affect global change.

5.

It is a wonderful idea to get involved in this charity!
Ask for a copy of the Save the Children Canada **6.** Volunteer Guide. You will make a difference in the lives of others as well as your own.

ISBN: 978-1-897164-42-6

F. Write "noun", "adjective", or "adverb" for the underlined clauses.

1. It doesn't matter <u>whether we go skating or skiing</u>.   _____

2. Richard says that he knows <u>where his budgie is hiding</u>.   _____

3. Is this the book <u>that Laurie has been looking for</u>?   _____

4. Dave has been taking guitar lessons <u>ever since he heard
    an amazing guitar solo on the radio</u>.   _____

5. Maggie is surprised <u>that Tom is so smart</u>!   _____

6. Sam's painting is the one <u>that has a blue house under an
    orange sky</u>.   _____

7. Kevin is frustrated <u>because he cannot find the most
    important ingredient for his latest culinary creation</u>.   _____

**G. Check the correct conditional sentences. Put a cross for the wrong ones
    and rewrite them on the lines.**

1. Tanya will stay indoors if it gets too cold outside.   ☐

    _____

2. If you had needed more paper, just tell me.   ☐

    _____

3. If you had put in garlic, this soup would have been awful!   ☐

    _____

4. I would not lose my turtle if I had kept an eye on it.   ☐

    _____

5. This picture will be more colourful if I were the one painting it.   ☐

    _____

6. "Let me know if you want more chicken broth," says Mom.   ☐

    _____

7. "If I'm not back in five minutes...well, just wait longer!" Kim says
    jokingly.   ☐

    _____

    _____

ISBN: 978-1-897164-42-6

H. Change this dialogue into the report structure.

"Did you know there'll be a special exhibit at the National Gallery of Canada in Ottawa?" Dave asked.

"No, I didn't," replied Shelley. "What's the exhibit?"

"It's an exhibit called 'Wilderness in the City', showing the works of Emily Carr."

"Emily Carr? Wow! She's my favourite Canadian artist."

"Mine too, actually. I love her spiritual paintings of the forests in British Columbia."

"She makes the wilderness look very mysterious."

"Romantic, too."

"So when is the exhibit?"

"It runs from March 3 to May 10. Do you want to go together?"

"Sure!"

"This Saturday, then?"

"Sounds perfect!"

_____

_____

_____

_____

_____

_____

_____

_____

_____

_____

_____

ISBN: 978-1-897164-42-6

ISBN: 978-1-897164-42-6

Section 3

Usage

ISBN: 978-1-897164-42-6

1 Choice of Words

Importance of Word Choice

Words help create images: the more precise and descriptive our words are, the more vivid images we can create.

Examples: *The injured boy walked away in pain.*

The injured boy <u>limped</u> off in pain. (walked unevenly with difficulty)

"Ouch! That hurts," said Simon.

"Ouch! That hurts," <u>wailed</u> Simon. (loud, high-pitched voice showing pain)

A. For each of the following "common" words, think of at least five words that are more specific or descriptive. Then use one of them to write a sentence of your own.

1. happy   _____

                      _____

2. cry   _____

                      _____

3. small   _____

                      _____

4. big   _____

                      _____

5. run   _____

                      _____

ISBN: 978-1-897164-42-6

6. nice _____

_____

7. beautiful _____

_____

8. good _____

_____

B. **Replace the underlined word or phrase in each sentence below with a more specific or descriptive one. Make any necessary structural changes.**

1. The <u>poor</u> man has gone without food for days. _____

2. The traffic was <u>slow</u> because of an accident. _____

3. The <u>big and tall</u> building belongs to Mr. Howard. _____

4. That's the <u>best</u> Greek food I've ever tried. _____

5. The mice <u>ran away</u> quickly. _____

6. He is driving an <u>old</u> car. _____

7. She was awakened by <u>a loud noise</u>. _____

8. The little boy <u>ate</u> the ice cream cone happily. _____

9. He <u>looked at</u> the painting for a long time. _____

10. The clowns were <u>funny</u>. _____

11. The principal thinks that our project is <u>good</u>. _____

12. It is <u>bad</u> to leave the puppy out in the cold. _____

ISBN: 978-1-897164-42-6

1

Pointers for Word Choice

When we go over our writing, we can ask ourselves:

- Have I used some common words repeatedly?
- Have I used some strong verbs or colourful phrases to grab the reader's attention?
- Have I chosen the most precise word?
- Have I used any captivating words?
- Can I replace a phrase with a more precise and descriptive word?

C. Revise the following text about whales by using words and phrases that are more precise or descriptive.

Whales are big; some whales can grow to 30 metres. Whales are mammals that once lived on land. They started living in water about 50 million years ago. Like all mammals, whales need to breathe air into lungs. Unlike us, whales breathe through blowholes on the top of the head. Baleen whales have two blowholes and toothed whales have one. Whales' respiratory system allows them to stay underwater for long periods of time without breathing. Some whales can stay underwater for up to two hours. When we breathe, we do not think about how and when to breathe. But whales have to decide when to breathe.

Like all other mammals, whales need to sleep, but they cannot fall asleep for too long since they need to stay conscious in order to breathe. Some scientists think that only one hemisphere of the whale's brain rests at a time. So, whales are never completely asleep. Scientists also think that whales usually sleep for eight hours, much like what we do.

160

ISBN: 978-1-897164-42-6

ISBN: 978-1-897164-42-6

2 Adding Emphasis

There are a number of ways to add emphasis to our sentences when we are expressing our opinions, disagreeing, making strong suggestions, or expressing annoyance.

Using the Passive Voice

The **passive voice** is used when focusing on the person or thing affected by an action. In general, the beginning of a sentence receives more attention, and by using the passive voice, we emphasize what happens to someone or something rather than who or what does something.

Example: *The manager expects all the reports to be submitted to him by the end of this week.*

All the reports are expected to be submitted by the end of this week. (Emphasis is on "all the reports", not the manager.)

A. Rewrite the following sentences in the passive voice to shift the emphasis.

1. The flood killed almost all the villagers.

   _____

2. The police caught the ringleader during the raid.

   _____

3. The firefighters finally put out the raging fire after more than five hours.

   _____

4. Someone removed the sculpture from the square in the heat of the night.

   _____

5. The coach told the players on the bench to step up their effort if they wanted to play more regularly.

   _____

   _____

ISBN: 978-1-897164-42-6

Inversion

Inversion is another way to add emphasis to a sentence. We do so by placing a prepositional phrase or other expression ("at no time", "little", "seldom", "never", etc.) at the beginning of the sentence, followed by inverted word order.

Example: *I never said you couldn't join us.*
   Never <u>did I say</u> you couldn't join us.

B. Use inversion to rewrite the following sentences.

1. I have seldom felt so helpless.

   _____

2. The police had hardly arrived at the scene when the car exploded.

   _____

3. He did not realize the magnitude of the problem.

   _____

4. We did not expect to be able to sweep the champion team.

   _____

5. She did not know that it was no longer a secret.

   _____

6. They rarely dined at the restaurants in the neighbourhood.

   _____

   _____

7. Keith does not know that he has been set up.

   _____

   _____

8. I have never seen a lobster this big!

   _____

   _____

 ISBN: 978-1-897164-42-6

Exceptional Use of "Do", "Does", and "Did"

We use these auxiliary verbs in positive sentences to emphasize something we feel strongly about. This form is also used to express something contrary to what another person believes.

Example: *He drove me home that night.*
He <u>did drive</u> me home that night. (emphatic)

C. Put "do", "does", and "did" in the following sentences to add emphasis.

1. We went to the haunted house on Halloween.

   _____

2. She knows how to solve the problem.

   _____

3. Fred apologized to Helen for embarrassing her.

   _____

4. The raccoon built a home in my garage.

   _____

5. I believe that we still stand a chance in the game.

   _____

6. The driver stopped to make sure he didn't hit anyone.

   _____

7. The magician performs for us every Saturday evening.

   _____

8. The principal asked me to help her out with the filing work.

   _____

9. We swim twice a week to keep fit.

   _____

ISBN: 978-1-897164-42-6

Cleft Sentences

Sentences introduced by "It is" or "It was" are often used to emphasize a specific subject or object. The introductory clause is then followed by a relative pronoun.

Example: *Mr. Coleman finally received the promotion.*

   It was Mr. Coleman who finally received the promotion.

Sentences introduced by a clause beginning with "What" are also used to emphasize a specific subject or object. The clause introduced by "What" is used as the subject of the sentence and is followed by the verb "to be".

Example: *After the game, we all needed a good, long shower.*

   After the game, what we all needed was a good, long shower.

D. Rewrite these sentences by using "It" or "What" to begin them.

1. He wanted a room all to himself.

   _____

2. Mary was elected captain, not Melissa.

   _____

3. Her brother ate half of the fruitcake.

   _____

4. They tried to make everyone happy.

   _____

5. I revealed the truth to the principal.

   _____

6. Heather had mistakenly taken the windbreaker home.

   _____

   _____

7. He must keep his chin up and start all over again.

   _____

   _____

ISBN: 978-1-897164-42-6

3 Words that Help Build Paragraphs

Paragraphs that Explain

In writing a paragraph to explain a certain issue, we often need to tell how or why something happens, and explore causes and effects of certain events.

A. Use the following words and phrases to write sentences of your own. They help explain the how's and why's as well as causes and effects.

1. since; thus

   _____

   _____

2. because; therefore

   _____

   _____

3. due to; hence

   _____

   _____

4. as a result of

   _____

   _____

5. if...then

   _____

   _____

6. as

   _____

   _____

ISBN: 978-1-897164-42-6

Paragraphs that Involve Sequencing

In a **sequencing paragraph**, we present a series of events based on time or describe a process step-by-step.

B. **Use the following words and phrases to write sentences of your own. They help you present your ideas in an orderly way.**

1. first, second, third...

   _____

   _____

   _____

2. then

   _____

   _____

3. in the beginning

   _____

   _____

4. at last

   _____

   _____

5. before; now

   _____

   _____

6. finally

   _____

   _____

ISBN: 978-1-897164-42-6

Paragraphs that Compare and Contrast

In writing a paragraph, we sometimes need to write about the similarities and differences between people, places, things, or ideas.

C. Use the following words and phrases to write sentences of your own. They help you compare and contrast people, places, things, or ideas.

1. similar to

_____

_____

2. in contrast

_____

_____

3. however

_____

_____

4. on the other hand

_____

_____

5. differs from

_____

_____

6. both

_____

_____

ISBN: 978-1-897164-42-6

D. Choose one of the following topic sentences and develop it into a paragraph.

- Like many other teenagers, Terry Fox was sporty and he enjoyed playing hockey.

- Last weekend, Dad and I went kayaking.

- Darren and Drew are twins but they are just so different.

- Sue and I are no longer on friendly terms.

- It was a hassle preparing for the trip.

Your Paragraph:

_____

_____

_____

_____

_____

_____

_____

_____

_____

_____

_____

_____

_____

_____

_____

_____

ISBN: 978-1-897164-42-6

4 Paragraphs

An essay is made up of **paragraphs**. In general, there are three types of paragraphs in an essay: introductory, supporting, and concluding.

The Introductory Paragraph

This is the beginning paragraph of our essay. It introduces the main idea in the form of a thesis statement. In the introductory paragraph, we provide some background information about the topic by using interesting facts, quotations, or definitions of important terms. A good **introductory paragraph** should capture the interest of the reader.

A. Write an introductory paragraph on one of the following topics. Begin with a thesis statement and support it with some background information.

- *The World as a Global Village*   • *My Favourite Summer Pastime*
- *My Hero*   • *Space Travel*   • *Hockey – the National Sport?*
- *Are We Getting More and More Materialistic?*

Topic _____

Introductory Paragraph

Thesis Statement: _____

_____

_____

Background Information: _____

_____

_____

_____

_____

ISBN: 978-1-897164-42-6

Supporting Paragraphs

Supporting paragraphs make up the main body of our essay. They help develop and expand the main idea that we introduced in the beginning paragraph. In writing the supporting paragraphs, we should:

- list the points that develop the main idea first;
- expand each point into its own paragraph; and
- support and illustrate each point with facts, details, and examples.

B. Based on the introductory paragraph that you wrote in (A), develop a plan for writing the supporting paragraphs.

Topic _____

Points for Developing the Main Idea

_____

_____

_____

_____

_____

_____

_____

_____

_____

_____

_____

_____

_____

_____

ISBN: 978-1-897164-42-6

C. Expand each of the points you listed in (B) into a paragraph. Support and illustrate each point with facts, details, and examples.

_____

_____

_____

_____

_____

_____

_____

_____

_____

_____

_____

_____

_____

_____

_____

_____

_____

_____

_____

_____

_____

_____

ISBN: 978-1-897164-42-6

The Concluding Paragraph

This is the last paragraph of the essay. It restates or summarizes the main idea. We use the **concluding paragraph** to create a sense that our essay is complete. In the concluding paragraph, we should:

- restate the strongest points of our essay that support our main idea;
- conclude our essay by restating the main idea in different words; or
- give our personal opinion or suggest a plan for action.

D. Compose two different concluding paragraphs for the topic you chose in (A). One is by restating the main idea in different words and the other, by giving your opinion or suggesting a plan for action.

Concluding Paragraph 1

_____

_____

_____

_____

_____

_____

Concluding Paragraph 2

_____

_____

_____

_____

_____

_____

ISBN: 978-1-897164-42-6

5 Clustering Ideas

Clustering

This is a process that helps us find inspiration in the connection among ideas – we jot down any words or phrases that come along without pondering whether or not they are relevant. At this stage, do not organize too neatly because that may impede the flow of ideas. Don't cross out anything either because we can't tell where an idea will lead us.

A. **In no more than ten minutes, think of as many words and phrases that relate to the following topic as possible. Jot down whatever words or phrases that come to your mind.**

Multiculturalism in Canada

ISBN: 978-1-897164-42-6

ISBN: 978-1-897164-42-6

The Cleaning and Organizing Process

Clustering helps us come up with ideas quickly, without any obstruction. However, not all the words and phrases are relevant. After clustering, therefore, we should start the **cleaning** and **organizing process**.

B. Work on (A) again, following the guidelines below.

- Study the words and phrases. Cross out those that you think are irrelevant.
- Draw lines to link up related groups of words and phrases.
- Add ideas that should have been included but weren't.
- Think of a thesis statement (the main idea) based on the cluster of ideas.

C. Write a thesis statement based on the cluster of ideas you developed in (A).

Thesis Statement

_____

_____

_____

_____

_____

D. Expand the groups of words and phrases into sentences. Add in transitional words to maintain a smooth flow.

_____

_____

_____

_____

_____

_____

ISBN: 978-1-897164-42-6

_____

_____

_____

_____

_____

_____

_____

_____

_____

_____

_____

_____

_____

_____

Read your thesis statement and the sentences that are developed from it. Do they flow logically and smoothly? Does your writing sound good to you?

_____

_____

_____

_____

_____

_____

_____

ISBN: 978-1-897164-42-6

6 Organization

The Importance of Organization

Good writing involves good **organization**: to present our ideas in a logical, easy-to-follow sequence. Good organization makes our writing more coherent and easier to understand. There are some common ways to organize our writing: chronological order, spatial order, topical order, and order of importance.

Chronological Order

In **chronological order**, events are arranged in the order in which they occur. We use transitions such as "then", "the next day", "a week later", "by January", and so on to link events together.

A. **Choose one of the following topics and think about what you want to write about. Organize your ideas based on the chronological order.**

A Day in the Life of a Policeman   **A Most Memorable Concert**
The Final Countdown   **My First Day as a Volunteer**

Topic _____

Organization of Ideas

_____

_____

_____

_____

_____

_____

_____

ISBN: 978-1-897164-42-6

Spatial Order

Spatial order is often used in descriptive writing. In spatial order, things are presented according to their physical position or relationships.

Example: *As he pushed open the door, he saw a man lying on the floor. Next to him was an empty wine bottle. The man seemed drunk.*

B. For each of the following topics, write a few sentences demonstrating the use of spatial order.

1. A boat trip on a waterway

   _____

   _____

   _____

   _____

   _____

   _____

   _____

2. The hockey rink where two teams were about to start the game

   _____

   _____

   _____

   _____

   _____

3. You visited your friend's house for the first time

   _____

   _____

   _____

   _____

   _____

ISBN: 978-1-897164-42-6

6

Order of Importance

In this pattern, items are arranged from least important to most important. Examples of transitions would include "more importantly", "the most challenging", "better still", "by far the largest", "even more difficult", and so on.

C. **Arrange the sentences below based on the order of importance. Join them using transitional words or phrases. Make any necessary changes to the sentences and add descriptions you feel necessary to make it an organized paragraph.**

- Toronto is the biggest city in Canada.

- There are many skyscrapers in downtown Toronto.

- The CN Tower stands at 553.33 metres.

- The CN Tower is the signature icon of the city.

- The CN Tower offers a spectacular panoramic view of the entire Greater Toronto Area.

- The CN Tower is one of the tallest free-standing structures in the world.

_____

_____

_____

_____

ISBN: 978-1-897164-42-6

Topical Order

This is an order based on the nature of the topic itself. For example, writing about a social issue might involve identifying the problem, describing how serious it affects society, and suggesting actions that could be taken to address the issue.

D. Write a simple plan of how you would write about the following topics based on the topical order.

1. Child Poverty

_____

_____

_____

_____

_____

_____

2. How to Build a Website

_____

_____

_____

_____

_____

3. Nunavut, Our Newest Territory

_____

_____

_____

_____

_____

ISBN: 978-1-897164-42-6

7 Clarity in Writing

A strategy to achieve clarity in our writing is to move from general to specific, from the past to the present, and from familiar to unfamiliar. We should avoid going from general to specific, and then specific to general, and general to specific again. This way of writing would confuse the reader.

A. Compare the two paragraphs below and answer the questions that follow.

1. When I was young, I liked going fishing with my dad. We often spent hours fishing in a lake near our home. It didn't matter how many fish we could catch. Both of us simply enjoyed the natural environment there – the trees, little creatures, the fresh air, and the tranquility. Now, the lake has changed a lot. There are fewer fish and the water seems to be more polluted.

2. My dad and I often spent hours fishing in a lake near our home. It didn't matter how many fish we could catch. I simply liked going fishing with him when I was young. Now, the lake has changed a lot. There are fewer fish and the water seems to be more polluted. In the old days, we simply enjoyed the natural environment there – the trees, the little creatures, the fresh air, and the tranquility.

Which one is easier to follow? Why?

_____

_____

_____

_____

_____

_____

ISBN: 978-1-897164-42-6

B. Rewrite the following paragraphs to make them easier to follow.

1. In the fall, Canada geese start migrating to warmer regions as far south as Mexico. They spend their summer in northern regions. Smaller geese tend to migrate in larger flocks than larger geese do, and season flocks tend to be made up of more geese than early season flocks. Canada geese migrate in flocks that vary in size.

_____

_____

_____

_____

_____

_____

2.

New Brunswick is the only officially bilingual province in the country. As a bilingual province, New Brunswick has a comprehensive parallel Anglophone and Francophone public school system from kindergarten to grade 12. It is one of Canada's three Maritime provinces. The majority of the people in New Brunswick are English-speaking. There are approximately 750 000 people living there. The French-speaking minority constitute about 35% of the population.

_____

_____

_____

_____

_____

_____

ISBN: 978-1-897164-42-6

Avoiding Multiple Negatives

We should avoid using multiple negatives because they tend to be difficult to understand. Change negatives to affirmatives wherever appropriate.

Example: *There is no point telling them not to do things that do no good to their health.*

It is pointless to tell them to stop doing things that harm their health. (better)

C. Rewrite the following sentences to improve clarity.

1. No one will pay attention to you if you do not speak with confidence and do not carry yourself properly.

_____

2. Not many people were interested since there was not enough publicity and the cast was not strong.

_____

3. They will not listen to you if you cannot provide any evidence to prove that you were not there.

_____

4. The guests did not expect that the dishes were not spicy and the drinks not exotic.

_____

Positioning Subordinate Clauses

We should avoid putting a subordinate clause into the main clause as this may make our idea difficult to follow.

Example: *The single-digit growth, when we factor in what has happened in the past three months, should be considered more than acceptable.*

When we factor in what has happened in the past three months, the single-digit growth should be considered more than acceptable. (better)

ISBN: 978-1-897164-42-6

D. Rewrite the following sentences to improve clarity.

1. We don't know, until we can get more details, whether or not we should proceed as planned.

   _____

2. The music, if you listen carefully to how the beginning is played, sounds like a piece composed by David Foster.

   _____

3. Everyone, including Mr. and Mrs. Schuler, is, although you may not know, ready to pitch in.

   _____

Using Action Verbs

Whenever possible, we should avoid using forms of "be" as the main verbs in our sentences and clauses. Try focusing on the actions we want to express and choose the appropriate verbs.

Example: *The coverage of the news in the National Express is more comprehensive than that in the Financial Daily.*

The National Express covers the news more comprehensively than the Financial Daily. (better)

E. Rewrite the following sentences using action verbs. Make any necessary changes.

1. Our meeting was for the discussion of two main issues: the endorsement of the plan and the amendment of the rules.

   _____

2. The proposal is now under consideration by the committee.

   _____

3. Upon arrival in Paris, we made the decision of starting our trip with a visit to the Eiffel Tower.

   _____

ISBN: 978-1-897164-42-6

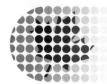

8 Narrative Writing (1)

What Is a Narrative?

Basically, a **narrative** is a story. It has a beginning, a middle, and an end. Centred upon a plot, a narrative moves through events, usually in a chronological order.

A. Rearrange the sentences so that they follow a chronological order.

1. I was standing in the middle of the bus next to a young lad in a red T-shirt. On Friday afternoon, I was riding home from school on a bus. She was dozing off, holding onto her handbag. It was very crowded, as everyone seemed to be hurrying home for the long weekend. An old woman was sitting opposite us.

_____

_____

_____

_____

_____

2. Tonight they would trick-or-treat to their hearts' content, raking in the goodies. The boys hurriedly put on their Halloween costumes while chattering away with delight in anticipation of one of their favourite days. Then they would all go back to Ken's home. It was a chilly night. His mom and dad would inspect their goodies before they could eat them. They couldn't wait for the festivities of the evening to begin.

_____

_____

_____

_____

_____

ISBN: 978-1-897164-42-6

The Power of Description

To make our writing interesting and captivating, we use **descriptions** to add details to the characters or events. Descriptions help our readers to form mental pictures as they read.

Example: *I was <u>walking</u> on the <u>road</u>...*

I was <u>strolling leisurely</u> on the <u>road leading to the small chapel</u>...

B.   Use descriptive words or phrases to add details to the following sentences. Change some of the words if necessary but do not change the main ideas.

1.   Caught in the rain, we were all wet.

   _____

   _____

2.   The boy asked the man for money.

   _____

3.   The boat sailed along the river.

   _____

4.   We went on a picnic to relax after a week of tests.

   _____

5.   There were only two occupants in the big house.

   _____

6.   My sister talked on the phone while I took a nap in my room.

   _____

7.   The carnival started after the mayor's speech.

   _____

8.   I opened the box and found a figurine inside.

   _____

ISBN: 978-1-897164-42-6

Use of Dialogue

Dialogue adds reality to our writing. It enhances the reader's sense of "being there". Be careful, however, not to put in dialogue for the sake of having dialogue. Dull dialogue is an instant turnoff.

Example: *The shopkeeper accused Josh of stealing a bag of candy.*

Grabbing Josh by the arm, the angry shopkeeper said, "What's in your pocket? Take it out, you little brat!"

C. Write dialogues based on the sentences given.

1. Tom's mother asked Tom to finish his assignment before watching the show. Tom didn't want to miss any part of the show and promised to work on the assignment as soon as the show ended.

   _____

   _____

   _____

2. The police officer stopped the stranger and asked for his identification. He suspected that the stranger was connected to a case of burglary.

   _____

   _____

   _____

3. Brad wanted very much to join the school baseball team. Mustering his courage, he approached Mr. Watson, the coach, and asked him for a chance to join the Saturday practice session.

   _____

   _____

   _____

ISBN: 978-1-897164-42-6

D. **Write about an incident that happened to you or anyone you know. It can be funny, scary, inspiring, or uplifting.**

Remember what you've learned:

- **Write chronologically**
- **Use descriptions**
- **Add in dialogues**

ISBN: 978-1-897164-42-6

9 Narrative Writing (2)

Selection of Significant Details

In narrative writing, we should not include every little thing that happened. A narrative is not an exact transcription. It is up to us to determine which parts of the experience are important. Include the details that are essential to getting your idea across. Omit those that are unrelated to, or are distracting from, the main idea.

A. Read the following paragraphs. Cross out the details that you think are unrelated to the main idea and should be left out.

When Helen Keller was 19 months old, she fell ill. Babies get sick easily, and like other parents, Helen's parents weren't too concerned about it at the beginning. They left Helen with the maid. Days passed but Helen didn't seem to get any better. Helen's parents started to worry and they took her to the doctor's. The doctor thought that it was "brain fever" that Helen was suffering from. In those days, brain fever was a deadly disease. To this day the nature of her ailment remains a mystery. Modern day doctors think it may have been scarlet fever or meningitis. Helen was, for many days, expected to die. Eventually, the fever subsided, and Helen's parents were relieved, believing that their daughter was well again.

However, Helen's mother soon noticed how her daughter was failing to respond when the dinner bell was rung or when she passed her hand in front of her daughter's eyes. It was evident that Helen's illness had left her both deaf and blind. What a tragedy for Helen! Imagine a child who can't hear or see for the rest of her life!

ISBN: 978-1-897164-42-6

B. Based on the following outline, write a paragraph about Helen Keller and her teacher, Ms. Anne Sullivan.

- Anne attempted to make Helen behave – led to more temper tantrums

- Anne punished Helen by refusing to "talk" (spelling words on her hands) with Helen

- Helen's behaviour gradually improved

- Anne led Helen to a water pump – pumped water over Helen's hand and spelled out the word "water" in Helen's free hand – finally understood the meaning of the word "water"

- All the way back to the house Helen learned the name of everything she touched – learned the spelling of 30 new words that day

_____

_____

_____

_____

_____

_____

_____

_____

_____

_____

_____

_____

_____

ISBN: 978-1-897164-42-6

Element of Conflict

A good story includes some kind of **conflict**, some complication that the main character (protagonist) runs up against. This could be an external struggle between two people, or it could be an internal conflict.

Examples: *Brad was the backup catcher and he wanted to prove that he could be a regular player. (internal conflict)*

Brad was the backup catcher and to get to be the regular player, he had to outplay Mike, the regular catcher. (external conflict)

C. **Write a paragraph about Nina to show the struggle within herself.**

Nina knew that it was Pat, her best friend, who had taken Mallory's brooch. She was in a dilemma: to stay mum or to tell Mallory.

_____

_____

_____

_____

_____

_____

_____

_____

_____

_____

_____

_____

ISBN: 978-1-897164-42-6

Climax

The **climax** of a story is defined as the place at which the conflict comes to a point of crisis, a high point in the tension, or an important turning point. After this high point, the narrative has some kind of resolution.

D. **Continue with your narrative about Nina. Write about her decision and what happened afterwards. Use dialogue to make the characters come to life.**

_____

_____

_____

_____

_____

_____

_____

_____

_____

_____

_____

_____

_____

_____

_____

_____

_____

_____

_____

_____

_____

_____

ISBN: 978-1-897164-42-6

10 Writing Reviews (1)

A **review** is a kind of descriptive article. The writer of a review gives his or her opinion about a subject – a book, a film, a restaurant, or a music CD. While a review is basically a subjective piece of writing, it also includes some objective elements.

Background Information (objective)

What?	The title of the book or the movie The name of the restaurant
Who?	The author of the book or the director of the movie The owner or chef of the restaurant
When?	The year the book was written or the release date of the movie The opening date of the restaurant
Where?	The setting of the book or the movie The location of the restaurant

Category (objective)

The genre of the book or the movie

The cuisine served at the restaurant

Description (objective)

The plot, characters, and themes of the book or the movie

The taste of the food

Evaluation (subjective)

The writer's comments and opinions based on his or her description

ISBN: 978-1-897164-42-6

A. Read the following review and label the various elements.

"*Mike Newell's adaptation of J. K. Rowling's* ← **A**
B → *children's fantasy – Harry Potter and the Goblet of* ← **C**
Fire – shows how Harry competed with three other ← **D**
senior students in the Triwizard tournament. The
stunning special effects vividly reproduce Harry's
adventurous world. I dare say that this is the best- ← **E**
ever Harry Potter movie in the series..."

A. _____

B. _____

C. _____

D. _____   E. _____

B. Write a brief review of a movie you have watched. Your review should contain the four elements: background information, category, description, and evaluation.

_____

_____

_____

_____

_____

_____

_____

_____

_____

Making Evaluations

To make an **evaluation**, we need to have a good understanding of all the relevant facts. We cannot, for example, make a fair judgement about a restaurant until we know the cuisine it serves, the choices available on its menu, the prices, and the decor.

Example: Although <u>fabulous</u> <u>Italian</u> food is offered at Grand Sicily, the
(positive opinion) (fact)

<u>slow service</u> would make you think twice before dining there again.
(negative opinion)

C. Put the following descriptive phrases in the relevant boxes.

ample portions	amusing dialogues	award-winning dishes
bland taste	elaborate costumes	exciting opening
slow service	fragmented plot	uncomfortable seats
stunning effects	unimaginable script	disappointing ending
aloof attitude	relaxed atmosphere	inspiring theme
slow tempo	predictable storyline	noisy atmosphere

Movie

Positive	**Negative**

Restaurant

Positive	**Negative**

ISBN: 978-1-897164-42-6

D. **Read the following restaurant review. Underline the words or phrases that express positive opinions and circle all those that express negative opinions.**

The Little Sicily

The Little Sicily is located in Fairview Centre Mall, 237 Fairview Blvd., Incline Village. It has been an Incline Village favourite for more than 20 years.

Family owned and operated, the service is friendly and the cozy restaurant feels as if you were at your friend's dining room, though the brown lacquer panels on the white walls look somewhat dull.

The Little Sicily serves a dozen pasta dishes and many pizzas, as well as chicken, veal, shrimp, and beef. Dinners include soup or salad, a vegetable, and olive-oil garlic bread. I tried their Seafood Portofino Special: a huge dish of assorted shellfish in a delicious red sauce — it was simply delicious!

And don't forget to try their homemade tiramisu, which is the best I've ever had! Prices are somewhat on the high side, though, but the quality is worth it.

I'd give it a rating of 4.8 out of 5! A must-try restaurant.

ISBN: 978-1-897164-42-6

11 Writing Reviews (2)

Making Evaluations

When giving our opinions, we can use weak descriptive adjectives to make **understatements** and strong descriptive adjectives to make **overstatements**.

An understatement is a weak description which is not forceful enough to express how important or serious something is.

An overstatement is a strong description which makes something more serious or important than it actually is.

Example:

weak ⟵──────────────────────────────⟶ strong

    an acceptable dinner   a great dinner   the best-ever dinner

    not a good movie   a boring movie   the worst movie this year

A. **Write the following adverbs of degree in the chart below. Put those that make statements stronger on the left and those that make statements weaker on the right.**

totally   very   slightly   rather   especially   quite   extremely

fairly   really   somewhat   reasonably   particularly

Stronger	**Weaker**

ISBN: 978-1-897164-42-6

B. Read the following restaurant review and insert suitable adverbs of degree where indicated to make it more forceful.

Superb Indian Cuisine

Indian Delight is a 1. ∧ popular restaurant that offers a 2. ∧ wide range of Indian cuisine. Located in Markham Mall, it is easily accessible by Highway 7, 404, or 401. I went there with three friends on Saturday evening at about seven and we were 3. ∧ surprised to find that the staff remained 4. ∧ polite and helpful despite the crowd waiting for tables.

The restaurant has superb food and a fun, casual atmosphere. It serves delicious lamb, chicken, vegetable, and seafood curries. Chai tea is free with all meals; it's a wonderful hot drink to enjoy with the meal. The tandoori grilled chicken we ordered was 5. ∧ delicious – not too spicy, but with a delicious blend of spices and freshly grilled to-order flavour. The chicken palak was 6. ∧ spicy, though – it was a bit much for the uninitiated. Of course if you love spicy food, this is the perfect dish for you. The naan breads are great for dipping in the entree sauces. We tried both the plain and garlic naan breads which were freshly baked and delicious.

There were a couple of things that 7. ∧ bothered us, though. The price was 8. ∧ high, as each of us had to pay more than $40 for the meal. And the service was 9. ∧ slow and we had to wait for a 10. ∧ long time between dishes. Other than that, the experience was 11. ∧ enjoyable. We had a 12. ∧ pleasant dinner and will certainly return for the superb food.

ISBN: 978-1-897164-42-6

C. Rewrite each of the following sentences as an overstatement by using stronger descriptive adjectives or phrases.

> *Example:* *It was a pleasant experience.*
>
> *It was the most memorable experience I had on the trip.*

1. I had an unusual encounter on my way to school.

   _____

2. Josh was sad when he heard about the mishap.

   _____

3. The portions were somewhat small.

   _____

4. Our school baseball team was defeated.

   _____

D. Rewrite each of the following sentences as either an understatement or an overstatement.

1. He was excited and proud to have been able to catch such a huge bass.

   Understatement: _____

   _____

2. That was simply the best-ever French cuisine I've enjoyed in my life!

   Understatement: _____

   _____

3. The slow tempo of the show made it rather boring.

   Overstatement: _____

   _____

4. Everyone enjoyed Kate's performance.

   Overstatement: _____

   _____

ISBN: 978-1-897164-42-6

E. Write a review of a movie you have seen. The following guide may help you plan your writing and organize your ideas.

1. Background information

    - What is the title of the film?
    - Who are the leading actors/actresses?
    - Who is the director?
    - When was the movie released?

2. The type of movie

    - What is the genre?
    - Who is the target audience?

3. The content of the movie

    - What is the plot?
    - What is the main theme?

4. Your evaluation

    - What is good about the movie – the plot, acting, costume, setting, special effects, etc.?
    - What is not so good?
    - What is your recommendation?

_____

_____

_____

_____

_____

_____

_____

_____

_____

_____

_____

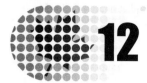

12 Argumentative Writing

Argumentation is everywhere because people do not always agree on what is true or what is fair. We try, for example, to convince our teachers and classmates to accept our ideas. We argue not because we are angry, but because arguing forces us to examine our own and others' ideas carefully. In fact, it causes us to:

- make judgements about an issue based on evidence;
- state our thoughts clearly and accurately;
- consider the ideas of others critically.

Argumentative Proposition

Like a thesis statement, an **argumentative proposition** states the main point. It sets the tone for the argument and enables the reader to know our stand. An argumentative proposition helps direct, develop, and monitor our thinking while writing.

A. Read the following argumentative propositions and decide whether or not you think the same. State why you agree or disagree.

1. The cellphone is more a curse than a blessing.

_____

_____

_____

_____

_____

2. Young people are getting less and less responsible.

_____

_____

_____

_____

_____

ISBN: 978-1-897164-42-6

3. Canada is the best country in the world.

_____

_____

_____

_____

_____

4. In this era of the Internet, schooling is a waste of time.

_____

_____

_____

_____

_____

Anticipating Opposition

Argument assumes **opposition** to our proposition. To win acceptance, we must not only explain and support our proposition, but we should also anticipate and overcome objections that the opposition might raise. To get an overview of the opposition's case relative to ours, we might consider drawing up a chart to compare the two sides of the argument.

Example:

Proposition: The cellphone is more a curse than a blessing.

For	*Against*
Encroach on our privacy	*Always stay connected*
Increase car accidents	*Hands-free talking*
A possible hazard to health	*Saves lives*
Become addicted	*Sensible use of cellphones*

Plotting our argument in a chart form allows us to see whether our case is strong. It also helps us consider how to refute the opposition's arguments.

ISBN: 978-1-897164-42-6

B. Choose one of the argumentative propositions in (A), except A1, and draw up a chart to compare the two sides of the argument.

Proposition: _____

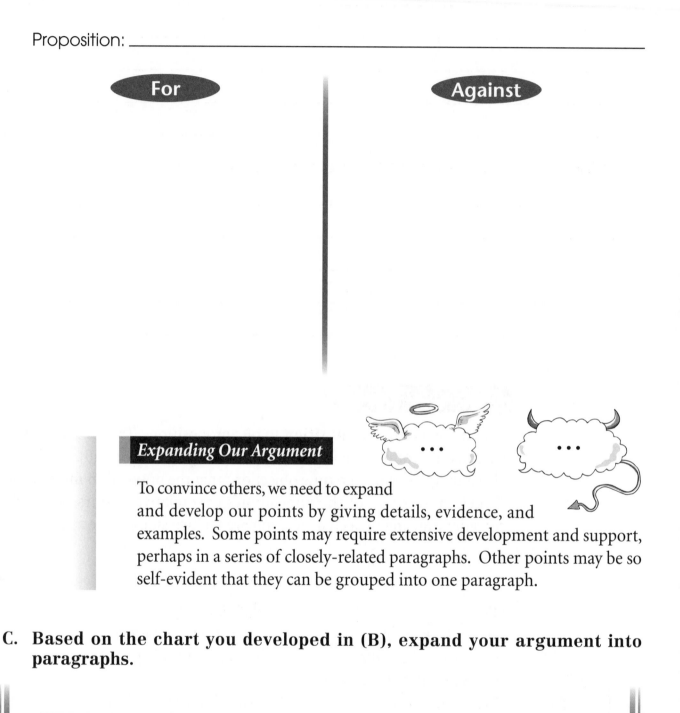

For

Against

Expanding Our Argument

To convince others, we need to expand and develop our points by giving details, evidence, and examples. Some points may require extensive development and support, perhaps in a series of closely-related paragraphs. Other points may be so self-evident that they can be grouped into one paragraph.

C. Based on the chart you developed in (B), expand your argument into paragraphs.

_____

_____

_____

_____

_____

ISBN: 978-1-897164-42-6

ISBN: 978-1-897164-42-6

13 The Editing Process (1)

Editing is an important process to ensure that our writing is the best that we would want it to be. In editing, we focus on two major areas:

The Language

- Check spelling.
- Check the use of punctuation.
- Make sure that each sentence has a subject.
- Make sure that subjects and verbs agree with each other.
- Check the verb tenses of each sentence.
- Read to see if each sentence makes sense.

Organization

- Check that there is a thesis statement that identifies the main idea of our writing.
- Make sure that our writing has an introduction, supporting paragraphs, and a concluding paragraph.
- Read to see if each paragraph has a topic sentence, supporting details, and a concluding sentence, or a sentence that leads to another paragraph.
- Cut out redundancy.
- Check if there is good transition between paragraphs.
- Read to see if our writing sounds right.

A. Correct the misspelled words and wrong punctuation in the following text on the abacus.

Before the adoption of the written Hindu-Arabic numeral system, the abacus was allready used widely as a calculation toll. In fact; it is still used by some merchants and clerks in China and Japan.

ISBN: 978-1-897164-42-6

The typical abacus is about 20 cm tall and it comes in various widths depanding on the application. It usually has more than seven rods, there are two beads on each rod in the upper deck and five beads each in the bottom. The beads are counted by moving them up or down towards the beam – Many Chinese and Japanese can use the abacus

at high speed, based on a set of technigues, to do multipication, division, addition, subtraction, and even square root and cubic root operations.

B. Correct the following faulty sentences.

1. Neither Jenny nor Danielle are held responsible for the accident.

   _____

2. Here are a list of things that I need to complete before school ends.

   _____

3. The only option left was to call the company and asked for the spare part to be shipped as soon as possible.

   _____

   _____

4. Greg don't seem to realize the gravity of the problem and keep the matter to himself.

   _____

   _____

5. Each of them want a share of the fruitcake but there just isn't enough for all of them.

   _____

   _____

ISBN: 978-1-897164-42-6

C. **Tighten up the following sentences by using phrases or subordinate clauses, or by breaking them into shorter sentences. Keep the original meanings.**

1. The hike took us five hours to complete and it was tiring but interesting and we saw quite a few rare species of insects.

_____

_____

2. The show was supposed to start at eight and somehow it was delayed but no one knew why and the audience became disgruntled.

_____

_____

3. The project took longer than we had expected and we had to burn the midnight oil for the whole week but we were unable to meet the deadline and luckily Mrs. Davis agreed to let us work on it for two more days.

_____

_____

4. The crowd gathered in front of the town hall and they demanded to meet with the mayor but the clerk came out and told them that the mayor was not in and they had to disperse or he would call the police.

_____

_____

5. The left fielder misread the ball and was too late to dive for it, and the ball just bounced to the far corner and the left fielder quickly picked himself up and ran to get it but by then the opposing team had already scored two runs.

_____

_____

_____

_____

ISBN: 978-1-897164-42-6

D. Edit the following paragraph. Focus on spelling and grammar. Rewrite the edited text on the lines provided.

Many of us must have used an abacus-like counting tool when we are at kindergarden or grade school. In fact, this form of "abacus" has used around the world as an aids in teaching the numeral system to small children. Each bead on this abacus have the same value. It can represent numbers up to 100. A significant educational adventage of using this counting tool is that it gave the child an awareness of the groupings of ten which are the foundation of the number system.

ISBN: 978-1-897164-42-6

14 The Editing Process (2)

Good Organization

Good organization ensures that we present our thoughts and ideas in a way that is easy for the reader to follow. In Unit 13, we introduced a checklist to see if our writing is well-organized:

- Check that there is a thesis statement that identifies the main idea of our writing.
- Make sure that our writing has an introduction, supporting paragraphs, and a concluding paragraph.
- Read to see if each paragraph has a topic sentence, supporting details, and a concluding sentence, or a sentence that leads to another paragraph.
- Cut out redundancy.
- Check if there is good transition between paragraphs.
- Read to see if our writing sounds right.

A. Organize the following groups of sentences in a logical sequence – beginning with a topic sentence, followed by supporting details, and a concluding sentence.

Group 1

- Wasn't that an ingenius idea?
- Have you ever wondered why a puck, and not a ball, is used in ice hockey?
- However, they soon found that the rubber ball used in field hockey was far too active on the hard ice surface.
- They came up with an idea – cut off the top and bottom of the ball to form the hockey puck!
- When hockey was first introduced to North America from Europe, players did use a rubber ball, much like what was used in field hockey.

ISBN: 978-1-897164-42-6

_____

_____

_____

_____

_____

_____

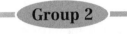

Group 2

- The most serious incident involving a spectator took place on March 18, 2002.

- A 13-year-old girl died two days after being struck on the head by a hockey puck deflected into the crowd at a National Hockey League game.

- It is extremely dangerous to players and spectators when they are struck by it. In fact, puck-related injuries at hockey games are not uncommon.

- During a hockey game, the puck can reach a speed of more than 160 kilometres an hour.

- As a result of this tragedy, glass panels sitting atop the boards of hockey rinks have been supplemented with mesh nets that extend above the upper edge of the glass.

_____

_____

_____

_____

_____

ISBN: 978-1-897164-42-6

B. Read the following paragraphs. Delete the words, phrases, and sentences that you feel are redundant.

1. In ice hockey, the puck is used instead of a ball. A puck is a hard, black disk made of rubber. A standard puck, which is made of rubber, is 25.4 mm thick, 76.2 mm in diameter, and weighs between 156 and 170 g in weight. Pucks are often marked with a team or league logo on one or both faces. We can find team or league logos on hockey pucks.

2. An American TV network once developed a "smart" puck. The "smart" puck had integrated electronics to track its position on screen. The electronics inside the puck was able to show the track clearly on screen. A blue streak traced the path of the "smart" puck across the ice. The streak would turn red if the "smart" puck was shot especially hard. This was an experiment to help viewers better follow the game by making the puck more visible. With the streak, the puck was more visible on screen.

3. The "smart" puck was first put to use in 1996, but traditional hockey fans did not like the idea. They thought that it spoiled the original form of the hockey game. And the "smart" puck did not meet its intended objective of drawing new viewers to the game either. Hockey fans did not like the "smart" puck and the "smart" puck was unable to draw more viewers. As a result, the experiment was stopped in 1998. The TV network discontinued using the "smart" puck.

ISBN: 978-1-897164-42-6

C. **Add a transitional sentence to better connect each of the following pairs of paragraphs.**

1. Did you know how the Stanley Cup came about? In 1888, the Governor General of Canada, Lord Stanley of Preston, attended a carnival and was impressed with the hockey games played there. Feeling that there was no recognition for the best team, Lord Stanley purchased a decorative bowl for use as a trophy.

   _____

   _____

   _____

   In 1893, the Stanley Cup was first awarded to the champion amateur team in Canada, Montreal AAA. It continues to be awarded today to the National Hockey League's championship team.

2. Ice hockey is played on a hockey rink. During normal play, there are six players from each team on the ice at any time. There are five players and one goaltender on each side. Players score goals by shooting the puck into the opponent's goal net.

   _____

   _____

   _____

   Other than the hockey stick, the players may also redirect the puck with any part of their bodies, subject to certain restrictions. Players may not intentionally bat the puck into the net with their hands.

3. Ice hockey is one of the fastest growing women's sports in the world, with the number of participants increasing 400 percent in the last ten years. Women's ice hockey was added as a medal sport at the 1998 Winter Olympics in Nagano, Japan.

   _____

   _____

   _____

   Although some people feel that the lack of bodychecking reduces the excitement of the game, others feel that without physical play, players can focus on their skating and puck-handling skills.

ISBN: 978-1-897164-42-6

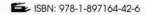 ISBN: 978-1-897164-42-6

Answers

ISBN: 978-1-897164-42-6

1 A Cross-Canada Culinary Tour

A. Alberta: barbecued steak and buffalo burgers
Manitoba: perogies
New Brunswick: fiddlehead soup
Newfoundland: baked codfish and blueberry pie
Nova Scotia: lobster
Saskatchewan: bannock and Saskatoon-berry pie
Quebec: baked bean casserole with a hint of maple
Vancouver: Chinese and South Asian food
Ottawa: poutine

B.

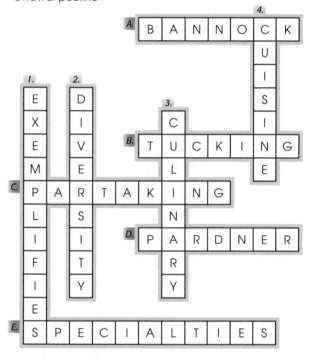

C. (Suggested writing)
Poutine:
The name "poutine" is likely an adaptation of the English word "pudding". The food originated in rural Quebec in the late 1950s, consisting of French fries topped with fresh cheese curds and covered with hot gravy and sometimes other additional ingredients. The fresh cheese curds are soft in the warm fries, without completely melting. Italian poutine, which is a variation of the original, substitutes gravy with "spaghetti sauce".

Perogy:
Perogies are crescent-shaped dumplings stuffed with cheese, mashed potatoes, cabbage, onion, meat, or with a fruit filling. They are fried or boiled until they float. They are then covered with butter or oil, and served with plenty of sour cream, topped with fried bacon or onions. Can you believe that a 7.6-metre perogy, complete with a fork, was unveiled in the village of Glendon, Alberta in 1993?

2 Surprising Stories about Sound

A. (Suggested writing)
Paragraph 1:
We must understand the dynamics of sounds and the features of the human ear to understand how we hear.

Paragraph 2:
Sound is a series of vibrations: collected by the pinna, magnified by the "ear bones", changed into messages by sensory cells in the cochlea, and sent to the brain.
Paragraph 3:
Humans actually do not hear very well compared to animals, like the elephant, which can hear sound levels as low as five hertz.
Paragraph 4:
The superior hearing of animals can be shown in their behaviour before natural disasters like the tsunami in 2004, when most animals in parks and zoos were reportedly unharmed.
Paragraph 5:
Animals in Thailand detected the low frequency sound of the tsunami long before it struck and instinctively headed uphill.
Paragraph 6:
We can hear sounds with a frequency between 20 and 20 000 hertz, but we gradually lose the ability to hear high frequency sounds as we age.

Your View
(Individual writing)

B. 1. H
2. C
3. G
4. B
5. A
6. F
7. D
8. E

C. (Individual writing)

3 If – a Poem by Rudyard Kipling

A. 1. A. self-confidence
2. B. acting on your dream without being controlled by it
3. A. the courage to take risks
4. A. how to develop the proper attitude towards life

Your View
(Individual writing)

B.

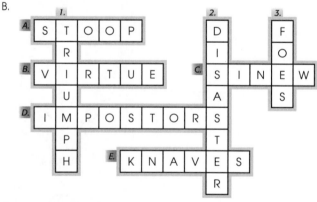

C. (Individual writing)

ISBN: 978-1-897164-42-6

4   Books Change Lives

A. 1. A portion of the royalties of the French publication has been donated to the Association for the Children of Ningxia, which assists the children of Ma Yan's home province.

    2-4. (Individual answers)

Your View

    (Individual writing)

B. (Individual writing)

C. (Individual writing)

5   Saint-Pierre and Miquelon

A. Paragraph One: A
Paragraph Two: A
Paragraph Three: B
Paragraph Four: A
Paragraph Five: A

B. (Individual writing)

C. (Individual writing)

6   Dealing with Stress in Japan

A. (Suggested writing)
Paragraph 1:
Stress can have an adverse effect on our bodies, which reacts by giving the "fight or flight" response.
Paragraph 2:
Long-term stress may cause premature aging or death, in addition to conditions such as insomnia and depression.
Paragraph 3:
Karoshi (death from overwork) has become a new epidemic in Japan.
Paragraph 4:
To help the stressed-out workers in Japan, some enterprising people have started to provide products and services such as nap salons.
Paragraph 5:
Nap salons offer sleep sessions which customers can enjoy at different prices.

Your View

    (Individual writing)

B. (Individual writing)

C. (Suggested writing)

  1. Yoga has a calming and soothing effect, as does meditation.

  2. You shouldn't work too late, and neither should you skip dinner.

  3. Mr. Watson doesn't know how to relax, and neither does his son.

  4. Patricia suffered from insomnia, and so did Jason.

  5. The workers took a quick nap after lunch, and so did I.

7   Canadians and Americans: What Makes Us Different?

A. 1. (Individual writing)

  2. When various groups of people headed out on their own to search for free land in the United States, they were settling in the west with little control from the government.

  3. The Canadian west was settled with more control from the government, which made effort to establish relations with the Aboriginal communities and traders before large-scale European settlement took place.

Your View

    (Individual writing)

B. (Suggested writing)

  1. The Pythons have lost five games in a row. By contrast, the Eagles seem invincible and are poised to win the division title.

  2. More has to be done to rectify the situation. In fact, we may need outside help to speed things up.

  3. He stands a good chance of getting the job. However the intervention of the chairman may complicate things.

  4. Don is always so helpful, amicable, and cheerful. By contrast, his brother Jason appears to be ill-tempered, impatient, and grumpy.

  5. Harrison does not show any sign of improvement whatsoever. In fact, he is getting more and more unreasonable.

C. (Individual writing)

8   The World of Third Culture Kids

A. 1. (Individual writing)

  2. (Individual answer)

  3. Some common problems are identity confusion, having parents who may minimize that sense of confusion, and anxieties from having to adapt to new cultures more often than the average child.

  4. A TCK has greater sensitivity and awareness of cross-cultural issues when raised by open-minded parents, is well-travelled and multilingual, more astute, and more comfortable internationally.

Your View

    (Individual writing)

B. Group 1: C ; B ; A
Group 2: B ; C ; A
Group 3: A ; C ; B

ISBN: 978-1-897164-42-6

C.

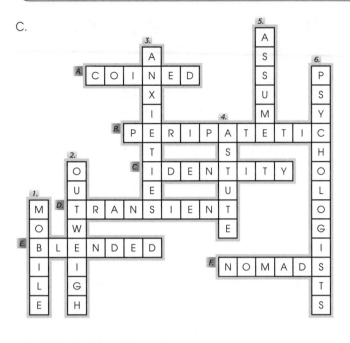

9 Beppu, Japan

A. 1. (Individual answer)
   2. "It" refers to the peaceful aesthetic of traditional Japanese culture.
   3. The country is located atop shifting tectonic plates and is therefore full of geothermal activity.
   4. They are hot springs and "bubbling mud pots" with water that range from being bright blue to having a deep rust colour.
   5. (Individual answer)

B.

C. (Suggested writing)
   1. A popular form of outdoor hot spring bath is the so-called waterfall, which comfortably massages your shoulders if you sit below it.

2. *Ashiyu*, which are shallow hot spring pools for bathing just your feet, are found in the streets of many hot spring resorts and can be used free of charge.
3. The hot springs in Japan are distinguished by the minerals dissolved in the water, with different minerals providing different health benefits, and all hot springs are supposed to have a relaxing and soothing effect.
4. When entering a Japanese house, you should take off your shoes at the entrance and change into slippers, which are usually provided by the host.

10 Music – Our Most Reliable Therapy

A. Paragraph 1:
   Whether it is used to soothe the beast in us, uplift us, or heal our bodies and minds, music has been our most reliable therapy since time began.
   Paragraph 2:
   In more recent years, music and its therapeutic qualities became an important element in nursing homes, hospitals, and mental health centres.
   Paragraph 3:
   In the burgeoning spa industry, the sound of music is being used to help us escape from an increasingly over-stimulating world. But there are some things to consider when choosing music to help you de-stress.
   Paragraph 4:
   Sound has the ability to create an emotional and physical response.

B. 1. Moms-to-be will snatch up CDs of *Baby Loves Beethoven* off store shelves.
   2. They can have mental connections to experiences in the listener's life that can make relaxation difficult, and the lyrics may act as trigger to memories.
   3. It is the kind of "New Age" music that features the sounds of nature, even the sounds of dolphins and whales in communication.

Your View
   (Individual writing)
C. (Suggested writing)
   1. an essential part
   2. to calm our animal nature
   3. the shocking experience in battles that affected the soldiers mentally and physically
   4. something to be taken lightly
   5. the fast-developing spa industry
   6. a world that is filled with more and more stimulation
   7. something that evokes memories
D. (Individual writing)

11 Rafflesia – a True Floral Wonder

A. (Individual writing)
B. (Suggested writing)
   1. We need air, water, and food to survive, but the growing population on Earth means we have to share our resources with more and more people. Moreover, the increasing amount of pollution produces acid rain that kills trees and harms the soil.

ISBN: 978-1-897164-42-6

2. Pandas were once found across China, Myanmar, and Vietnam, but today, they number fewer than 1000, and are believed to be found in only the mountain ranges in southwest China. There are only about 220 left in the Qinling Mountains, where the panda's habitat is fragmented by development.

C. (Individual writing)

12 Ethics in Science: Cloning and Genetic Modification

A. Benefit:
- may help infertile couples produce children
- may put an end to many diseases
- stem cells from cloned embryos may lead to medical advances

Concern:
- may produce unhealthy and malformed children
- cross-species transfers may create new risks
- people may not know what exactly they are eating
- new "species" may change the balance of nature in an ecosystem

Your View
(Individual writing)

B.

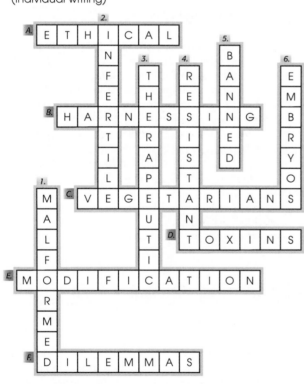

C. (Individual writing)

13 The World of Tea

A. black:
- withered, fully oxidized, and dried
- makes a strong, amber-coloured brew
- examples are English Breakfast and Darjeeling

white:
- the least processed
- withered and dried by steaming

green:
- not oxidized
- withered and then dried
- has a pale green / golden colour and delicate taste

oolong:
- in between black and green tea in colour and taste
- very popular in China
- referred to as "Champagne of Teas"

Your View
(Individual writing)

B. 1. Earl Grey tea
2. "chai" tea / Indian masala
3. bubble tea
4. Matcha

C. (Individual writing)
D. (Individual writing)

14 Living with Robots

A. 1. Japan has the most rapidly aging population and its industrial sector is creating robotic devices to make life easier for the elderly. Some have even gone mainstream, like the "automatic washing device" initially used in nursing homes.
2. The senior population will outgrow the younger one due to Japan's declining birthrate and therefore robots will become essential in taking care of the elderly.
3. (Individual writing)

Your View
(Individual writing)

B. (Suggested writing)
1. With the world's most rapidly aging population and a declining birthrate, the government and the private sector in Japan are turning to the manufacturing of robots as a solution.
2. Robots are not only industrially useful but also educational. Manufacturers such as LEGO are making robot kits for children to build their own robots, thereby stimulating their creativity and interest in exploring science.
3. Robots are best used in environments that are dangerous for humans. This is why they are often used in bomb disposal, underwater tasks, mining, and for cleaning toxic waste.

C. (Individual writing)

ISBN: 978-1-897164-42-6

15 The Nobel Prizes

A.

Achievement	Laureate	Year of Award
Discovery of radium and polonium	Marie Curie	1911
Research into chemical bonding	Linus Pauling	1954
Research into radiation phenomena	Marie Curie and Pierre Curie	1903
Synthesis of new radioactive elements	Irène and Frédéric Joliot	1935
Discovery of radioactivity	Antoine Henri Becquerel	1903
Founding of International Campaign to Ban Landmines	Jody Williams	1997
DNA-sequencing of nucleic acids	Frederick Sanger and his colleague	1980
Research on semiconductors	John Bardeen and his two colleagues	1956
Research into superconductivity theory	John Bardeen	1972
Research into structure of proteins	Frederick Sanger	1958

Your View
   (Individual writing)
B. (Individual writing)
C.

16 Another "Ice Age" on the Way?

A. 1. There is an increase in carbon dioxide emissions and the resulting "greenhouse" effect.
   2. There was significant hardship like the crop failures in parts of Europe when glaciers in Norway advanced onto farmland.
   3. The Gulf Stream "conveyor belt" has a warming effect on northern Europe.

   4. The Gulf Stream "conveyor belt" was stopped, ceasing its warming effect on northern Europe.

B.

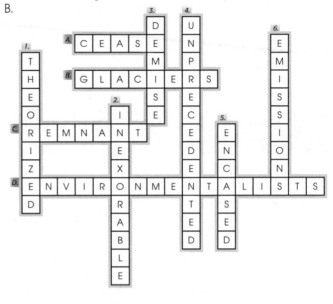

C. (Individual writing)

17 Special Olympians

A. 1. It is the conventional method of doing the high jump, by jumping over the bar head first, invented by Richard Fosbury at the 1968 Olympic Games.
   2. Those who are eligible are at least eight years old, identified by an agency or professional as having intellectual disabilities, cognitive delays, or significant learning or vocational problems due to cognitive delay.
   3. The Special Olympics not only organizes the games but also provides athletic training for more than 2.25 million children in over 150 countries.

Your View
   (Individual writing)
B. (Individual writing)
C. (Individual writing)

18 The Story of "Room to Read"

A. (Suggested writing)
   Paragraph One:
   While vacationing in the mountains of Nepal, John Wood, a Microsoft business executive, was saddened to discover that a school in the area had very few books.
   Paragraph Two:
   John asked friends by e-mail to send old children's books to his parents' home and received more than 3000 books within weeks. A year later, he and his father brought them to the school in Nepal.
   Paragraph Three:
   John decided to quit his job to help the world's poor children, making it his personal mission.

ISBN: 978-1-897164-42-6

Paragraph Four:
Some people tried to change his mind but John reminded himself what his dad once said: do what you think is the right thing and answer only to yourself.

Paragraph Five:
John set up a charity called "Room to Read" in 2000, building schools and funding scholarships in various countries in Asia. Programs will soon be starting in South Africa and Latin America as well.

Your View
   (Individual writing)

B.

C.   (Individual writing)

ISBN: 978-1-897164-42-6

Section 2 — # Answers

1 Verbs with Prepositions

A. 1. for 　　2. with ; on 　　3. about
4. at 　　5. for ; down 　　6. of
7. about 　　8. from 　　9. into
10. to 　　11. on 　　12. of
13. to ; for 　　14. on 　　15. to
B. 1. to 　2. to 　3. with 　4. at
5. to 　6. of 　7. at 　8. at
9. on 　10. to 　11. with 　12. at
C. (Individual writing)
D. 1a. stood down
　b. stand for
　c. stood in
　d. stand by
　2a. get along
　b. get down to
　c. get through
　3a. talked back
　b. talk ; into / out of
　c. talk ; into
E. (Individual writing)

2 Non-finite Verbs

A. designing – gerund
to plan – infinitive
to sew – infinitive
to make – infinitive
doing – participle
studying – participle
buying – gerund
choosing – gerund
putting – gerund
to learn – infinitive
exhausted – participle
running – gerund
to find – infinitive
to spend – infinitive
making – participle
B. 1. exhausted 　2. winning 　3. Speeding
4. Frightened 　5. Surrounded 　6. running
7. rising 　8. Satisfied 　9. exciting
10. trapped 　11. finished 　12. entertaining
C. 1. Losing the eighth inning upset the game plan.
2. Laughing relieves stress and lifts your mood.
3. Increasing the use of fuel leads to more pollution.
4. He sustained severe injury as a result of falling from the horse.
5. Jumping over the ditch can be dangerous.
D. (Individual writing)
E. (Individual writing)

3 More on Adjectives

A. 1. a small, old wooden house
2. the bright, little, round yellow dots
3. a charming, tall Canadian lady
4. an attractive, exquisite silver ornament
5. the well-built young athlete
6. the soiled, old blue shirt
7. an antique, brown wooden chair
B. 1. After an hour's walk, we finally reached a beautiful, small old chapel.
3. They showed me a big, sparkling oval gemstone.
4. Mr. Buffet bought her a new, black silk scarf.
6. She likes wearing that tight, pink leather coat.
C. (Individual writing)
D. (Individual writing)
E. (Individual writing)
F. 1a. those who had something to do with the matter
　b. worried, anxious
　2a. attending the meeting
　b. current
　3a. conscientious
　b. entrusted with the case

4 More on Adverbs

A. (Suggested writing)
1. How can I start this engine?
2. Where did you get it?
3. How long did it take you to complete it?
4. When did you arrive?
5. How much did it cost you?
6. How often does he go to the supermarket?
7. Why didn't they show up?
8. How confident are you in completing it on time?
B. 1. This is the auditorium where they ran the seminars.
2. The principal did not understand why she declined the offer.
3. They are planning to build a park where the old church once stood.
4. Mr. Sutherland came when they were having a heated debate.
5. The police wanted to know why she had not come forward earlier.
6. They had a trip in the summer when I was in South Africa.
7. We met at the café where Margaret worked.
8. He explained to his parents why he wanted to leave for Rome.
C. (Suggested writing)
1. Surprisingly, he turned out to be the winner.
2. Ideally, we would have at least 18 months for the project.
3. Honestly, I can't think of any solutions to this problem.
4. She is undoubtedly the best person to take up the assignment.
5. Obviously, Mrs. Kennedy will continue to coach the team.
6. The plan doesn't work economically.
7. Apparently, Ms. Fields did not know anything about it.
8. Theoretically, the waste can be recycled and reused.
D. (Individual writing)

5 Compound Words

A. (Individual answers)
B. 1. COM 　2. 　3. COM
4. COM 　5. COM 　6. COM
7.
C. (Suggested answers)
1. My uncle owns a six-acre farm.
2. The developer has decided to construct a twenty-storey building.

ISBN: 978-1-897164-42-6

3. The fire-resistant door looks similar to the other doors in the same building.
4. The tree-lined road leads to the cathedral.
5. Mr. Saunders managed to secure an interest-free loan.
6. We were greatly disappointed by his way-below-average performance.
7. The million-dollar project was completed on schedule.
8. Nothing was accomplished after the four-hour-long meeting.

D. (Individual writing)

E. 1. vice-principals
   3. man-hours
   5. family names
   7. bills of fare
   9. gateways
  11. winter festivals
   2. sergeant majors
   4. masters of ceremony
   6. ladies-in-waiting
   8. teacher librarians
  10. editors-in-chief
  12. merry-go-rounds

F. 2. well-being
   4. extraordinary
   9. wax museum
  11. in-house
   3. year-end
   5. also-ran
  10. home office
  12. underdeveloped

G. (Individual answers)

6 Frequently Confused Words

A. (Individual writing of sentences)
1. advice   2. affect   3. already
4. altogether   5. among   6. sow
7. alter   8. sight   9. raise

B. <u>badly</u> ; bad
<u>except</u> ; accept
<u>presence</u> ; present
<u>than</u> ; then
<u>between</u> ; among
<u>Beside</u> ; Besides

C.
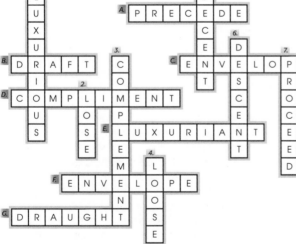

D. (Individual writing)

7 Conjunctions: Coordinating and Correlative

A. 1. and ; but / yet ; and   2. for
3. or   4. but ; for
5. or   6. and
7. and ; and ; and   8. or
9. but / yet ; or

B. (Suggested writing)
1. The committee members were divided on this matter but they agreed that it had to be settled as soon as possible, and they wanted to invite an accountant to study it.
2. The project is scheduled to be completed by the end of this month but many issues remain unresolved, and a delay seems inevitable.
3. They are given two options: they can call off the match or they can play the game after school, but they have to let the principal know their decision before noon.
4. By the time we reached the resort, everyone was exhausted. The first thing we wanted to do was to take a shower and go to bed, but before doing that, we had to wait for our leader to allocate our rooms.
5. Apparently the sign pointed to southeast; we followed it but we reached a deserted place, and it was not the town indicated on the map.

C. 1. either ; or / neither ; nor   2. not only ; but also
3. Whether ; or   4. either ; or
5. Neither ; nor   6. whether ; or
7. neither ; nor   8. either ; or
9. Not only ; but ; also   10. whether ; or

D. 1. This painting is not only artistic but also priceless.
3. I think neither Greg nor Paul should be held responsible for the mistake. They were there only as helpers.
4. Not only did he lie but he also took away the books from the library.
5. She said that she would either give you a call or send you an e-mail to explain everything.

E. (Individual writing)

8 A Review on Punctuation

A. 1. They had one common goal: to be able to complete the project by the end of the month.
2. By the time we reached the station, the train had already departed and there was only one way to make it in time: take a cab to go all the way to Townsville.
3. Everyone was taken by surprise; they did not know what to do next.
4. He let Mr. Belinsky read his script; it was the first script that he wrote.
5. Gary sensed that something had gone wrong: the dogs were barking fiercely.
6. The committee was made up of the following members: Mrs. Saunders, the librarian; Ms. Stewart, the school secretary; Mr. Dole, our vice-principal.
7. Photosynthesis is the synthesis of sugar from light, carbon dioxide, and water; oxygen is generated as a waste product.
8. They came up with a contingency plan: enlist the help from the neighbouring schools.

ISBN: 978-1-897164-42-6

9. We tried to dissuade him from doing it; he went ahead anyway.
10. Before leaving, make sure all the lights are turned off; it is the least you can do to conserve energy.
11. He did not admit his mistake: that he had forgotten to make payment on time.
12. The organizers hope to raise enough funds for the research: fifty thousand dollars at least.
13. Because of the storm, we cancelled the trip; I was a little disappointed.

B. 1. Samuel Langhorne Clemens (1835 – 1910) was a famous American humorist and writer better known by his pen name – Mark Twain.
2. Twain is most noted for his novels "The Adventures of Huckleberry Finn" and "The Adventures of Tom Sawyer" among other works.
3. Mark Twain had a funny quotation: "I have never taken any exercise except sleeping and resting."
4. Twain is often referred to as "the father of American literature".
5. The word "twain" is an archaic term for "two".
6. When Twain was four, his family moved to Hannibal, a port town on the Mississippi River – the place which later inspired him to write "The Adventures of Huckleberry Finn".
7. "Advice for Little Girls" (1867) was Twain's first published fiction.
8. Ernest Hemingway, another famous American writer, is best known for his novel "The Old Man and the Sea".
9. Hemingway's style guide was : "Use short sentences. Use short first paragraphs. Use vigorous English."
10. In 1920, Hemingway took a job at a newspaper in Toronto – the *Toronto Star*.
11. Many critics touted Hemingway's "A Clean, Well Lighted Place" as one of the best stories ever written.
12. Hemingway once said: "All modern American literature comes from one book by Mark Twain called 'Huckleberry Finn'."

C. (Suggested answers)
Most plants are able to synthesize food – a process called "photosynthesis" – directly from inorganic compounds using light energy (for example, from the sun) instead of eating other organisms or relying on nutrients derived from them.

Plants absorb light primarily using the pigment chlorophyll, which is why most plants are green in colour. Although all cells in the green parts of a plant have chloroplasts, most of the energy is captured in the leaves. The cells in the interior tissues of a leaf (called the mesophyll) contain about half a million chloroplasts for every square millimetre of leaf.

Do you know why chlorophyll looks green? Chlorophyll looks green because it absorbs red and blue light, making these colours unavailable to be seen by our eyes. It is the green light (which is not absorbed) that finally reaches our eyes, making chlorophyll appear green.

The surface of the leaf is uniformly coated with a water-resistant waxy cuticle: to protect the leaf from excessive evaporation of water. It also decreases the absorption of ultraviolet light to reduce heating.

D. Christopher Columbus (1451 – 1506) was an Italian-born Spanish explorer who sailed across the Atlantic Ocean in 1492 in the hope of finding a route to India (mainly for spice trade). He made four trips to the Caribbean and South America between 1492 and 1504.

On his first trip, Columbus led an expedition with three ships and about 90 crew members. They set sail on August 3, 1492 from Palos, Spain. On October 11, 1492, they spotted the Caribbean islands off southeastern North America. Columbus thought that he had made it to Asia, and called this area the "Indies", and its inhabitants "Indians".

Columbus also explored the northeast coast of Cuba and the northern coast of Hispaniola by December 5. There, one of his ships ran aground and had to be abandoned. He was received by the natives there, who allowed Columbus to leave some of his men behind. Columbus founded a settlement and left 39 of his men there. Then he headed for Spain, but another storm forced him into Lisbon, Portugal. After spending more than one week in Lisbon, he set sail for Spain. Word of his finding the New World soon spread throughout Europe.

Review 1

A. 1. at   2. up   3. to
4. to   5. to   6. from
7. to   8. to   9. into
10. with

B. 1. infinitive   2. neither   3. infinitive
4. gerund   5. neither   6. infinitive
7. gerund   8. neither

C. 1. In my dream, I saw a tiny red house across the street.
2. The little brown porcupine in the cartoon will not stop poking her friend!
3. This museum houses a lot of beautiful Canadian furniture from the 1800s.
4. Jim wants to see if his grandmother still has her old, soft colourful quilt.
5. Jack is the name of my cute, five-year-old American cousin.

D. 1. where   2. when   3. How
4. why   5. why   6. where
7. where

E. 1. seat belts   2. farmhands
3. panhandlers   4. passersby
5. road maps   6. mailboxes
7. middle names   8. close-ups
9. doggy bags   10. high schools
11. police stations   12. guests of honour
13. waffle cones   14. brothers-in-law

F. 1. advise – give someone advice
advice – opinion about what should be done
2. site – place used for an activity, a building, or a town
sight – act of seeing; spectacle
3. alter – modify the style or size of something
altar – table or stone for offering to a god
4. affect – touch the feelings of someone; influence
effect – result or consequence of an action
5. counsel – formally given advice; consultation
consul – person appointed by a country to live in a foreign city to foster understanding and promote trade

G. (Individual writing)

H. 1. or   2. but / yet ; and
3. for   4. or ; and
5. Neither ; nor   6. either ; or
7. but ; or   8. either ; or

ISBN: 978-1-897164-42-6

9. not only ; but also   10. but ; and

I. (Suggested answers)

Iceland can be a challenging country for engineers, not because of the frozen barrens, steam hissing from geothermal vents, bizarrely shaped lava rocks, or even volcanoes spouting fire. It is challenging because of the spirit folk lurking in the land.

Though Iceland is the most geographically remote of all European countries – being a tiny island just below the Arctic Circle – it is technologically advanced and highly literate: the literacy rate is 100 per cent! Yet Icelanders are also pretty serious about other-worldly beings, like gnomes, trolls, elves, lovelings, light-fairies (sisters to Tinkerbell), and a unique species called "huldufolk", or "hidden people". More than half of all Icelanders believe they may really exist. As noted by Arni Bjornsson, who is the head of ethnological studies at the National Museum of Iceland, "Even hard-headed engineers, who say they don't hold with superstition, will build a road around a certain hill or boulder rather than take the risk of offending elves." In fact, highway engineers in recent years have been forced to reroute roads around supposed elf dwellings.

So, why do Icelanders believe that they share their abode with tiny and hidden creatures? Here is one theory from Olafur Ragnar Grimsson, the country's president: it is because of Icelanders' abiding sense of loneliness and isolation. Icelanders are few in number, he explains, so they double their population with tales of elves and fairies. Of course this doesn't seem to make sense, but as Arni Bjornsson says, "It is hard to be totally scientific in a country as spectacularly strange as ours."

9 Phrases

A. 1. several small stars within the big star
2. The police ; an accident involving a stolen truck
3. The unexpected heavy snowstorm
4. Everyone in Mrs. Templeton's class ; a goodie bag
5. Several men swimming towards the lighthouse
6. The volunteers to help organize the event ; a meeting
7. His office ; that building across the street
8. The coach ; those failing to complete three laps ; their practice
9. a man standing right behind him
10. All the players of the opposing team ; a photoshoot

B. 1. We spent our weekend in a well-equipped houseboat.
2. On his way to school, he came across a dog with a backpack on its back.
3. Anyone wanting to join the team will have to undergo a selection process this weekend.
4. The $60-package includes all the accessories.
5. Those failing to comply with the rules will be penalized.
6. The exhausted pitcher missed the strike zone time and again.
7. The documentary featuring an hour-long interview with various environmentalists lasts almost two hours.
8. The town between Meadowville and Bloomsfield has a population of about 1000.
9. The team had a celebration attended by more than 10 000 fans at the stadium. /
The team had a celebration at the stadium attended by more than 10 000 fans.

10. Simon picked up a bottle with a message in it.
C. (Individual writing)
D. (Suggested writing)
1. Sharks have a keen sense of smell, with some species able to detect as little as one part per million of blood in seawater!
2. Sharks' eyes, having a tissue called tapetum lucidum, are well adapted to the marine environment.
3. However, some species, including the Great White Shark, do not have these membranes and they roll their eyes backwards to protect them when striking their prey.

10 Voice and Mood

A. Dodge ball is a fun game enjoyed by grade school children. A big, rubber ball is used and thrown at the players inside the circle.
The ball can only be thrown
If the ball is thrown
If a player in the circle is hit
B. (Suggested writing)
Grade school children enjoy the fun game of dodge ball. The players on the outside use a big, rubber ball and throw it at the players inside the circle.
They can only throw the ball
If a player throws the ball
If the ball hits a player in the circle
C. (Suggested writing)
1. The fire was put out by the firefighters in less than an hour.
2. The annual meeting will be held as scheduled.
3. The pamphlets were handed out to all the Grade 8 students by the teacher.
4. All borrowed books should be returned to the library before noon today.
5. A baby whale was seen about a mile off the shore.
6. Janet was awarded The Best Student of the Year Award by the principal.
7. Strangely, we were never approached by them.
8. The show was considered one of the best they had ever seen.
D. 1. IND   2. IND   3. SUB   4. SUB
5. SUB   6. IMP   7. IND   8. SUB
9. IMP   10. IND   11. SUB   12. IMP
E. 1. Let me have it as soon as possible.
2. Do not waste any more time on the minor details.
3. Please contact Mrs. Jones on my behalf.
4. Buy it online if you want to save time.
5. Bear right and turn left when you see the sign "Snowview".
F. (Individual writing)

11 More on the Passive Voice

A. 1. Can you tell me where the party is held?
3. They did not know if the matter had been settled.
4. We are given a second chance to do the experiment. The findings have to be submitted by Wednesday.
B. (Suggested writing)
1. The space shuttle will be launched after the problem has been fixed.
2. The problem would have been solved if I had been given the formula.

ISBN: 978-1-897164-42-6

3. Food and shelter were desperately needed by the refugees.
4. Our project has to be redone as it is considered too sketchy.
5. I was woken up by the storm in the wee hours of the morning.
6. No one was allowed to enter the premises without authorization.
7. The woman had been shot twice before the robber was gunned down by the police.
8. If the deadline was postponed, the project would be finished in time.

C. (Suggested writing)
1. Mr. Shaffer had his bathroom renovated.
2. We had the assignment completed before the deadline.
3. She thinks she can get all the forms filled out in an hour.
4. He wants to get the broken windows fixed.

D. 1. Our school is run-down and it needs renovating.
2. He did not realize that the food needed reheating.
3. The floor was so dirty that it needed scrubbing.
4. The wild horse needs taming before anyone can ride it.

E. (Suggested writing)
Many sportswriters, coaches, and fans have also called him "the greatest hockey player ever".

He has also been called "the greatest hockey player ever" by many sportswriters, coaches, and fans.

People attributed Gretzky's dominance throughout his career to the amount of time he put into his practice.

Gretzky's dominance throughout his career was attributed to the amount of time he put into his practice.

People often described him as someone who "seems to have eyes in the back of his head".

He was often described as someone who "seems to have eyes in the back of his head".

12 A Review on Sentences

A. (Suggested writing)
1. Compound sentence:
They finally reached the destination but the other teams were already there.
Complex sentence:
Although they finally reached the destination, the other teams were already there.
2. Compound sentence:
The oil tank started leaking; our car could stop any minute and we would be forced to walk our way across the deserted plain.
Compound-complex sentence:
Because the oil tank started leaking, our car could stop any minute and we would be forced to walk our way across the deserted plain.
3. Simple sentences:
We searched everywhere. We were unable to find the key. Without the key, there was no way we could enter the house.
Compound-complex sentence:
Although we searched everywhere, we were unable to find the key and there was no way we could enter the house.

B. (Individual writing)
C. (Suggested writing)
1. How spectacular the firework displays are!
2. Submit by Friday or else you'll be penalized.

3. Mrs. Carter remarked that John was disrespectful.
4. Why didn't he tell his mother about it?
5. Will the guests stay overnight?
6. Patrick asked if Simon had been to Prince Edward Island before.
7. Teresa felt that it was a splendid evening.
8. Is there any other course of action to take?
9. Watch out for the car!

D. (Individual writing)

13 Dependent Clauses as Nouns, Adjectives, and Adverbs

A. (Individual writing)
B. 1. that he needed to seek Mr. Jenkin's permission before going ahead with the scheme
2. Whatever you do
3. that their team could score in the last 60 seconds
4. Whether or not they could make it
5. which train passed by the little border town

C. (Individual writing)
D. (Individual writing)
E. (Individual writing)
F. 1. ADV   2. N   3. ADJ
   4. ADJ   5. N   6. ADV

14 Report Structures

A. 1. Jen's mother told her to take the pup for a walk.
2. Linda asked Sean if he wanted some more coffee.
3. Our teacher told us that the practice would start at 7:00 p.m. sharp.
4. Mavis replied indifferently that she didn't know who I was referring to.
5. The coach asked if he had ever tried the diving catch.
6. The guide told the worried tourists that they might not be able to reach there before midnight.

B. (Individual answers)
C. (Suggested writing)
1. The coach said to the team, "Practise for another two hours. Based on your current performance, I don't think you have a chance of winning the game."
2. "I'm new here. I didn't know the rules," he explained to the manager. "Could you give me another chance? I promise that I will not do that again."
3. "Thank you. It was such a wonderful evening," Mariam thanked Dave when the party was over. "I had a wonderful time too," Dave replied. "Could I pay you a visit sometime next week?"

D. (Suggested writing)
Terry did not understand why Ben thought it that way. When Heather asked him to explain what way he was referring to, Terry told her that Ben thought that they ganged up on him. Heather wanted to know if they really did so. In reply, Terry denied it and remarked that Ben simply isolated himself. Heather felt that they must have done something that had made him think that they were ganging up on him. Terry thought that it was possible. Heather then suggested that he invite Ben to their gathering. However, Terry doubted if Ben would come. Heather felt that he should try or he would not know. Finally, Terry agreed to give it a try.

ISBN: 978-1-897164-42-6

15 Conditional Clauses (1)

A. (Individual writing)
B. 1. will stand 2. will make 3. will find
   4. will be 5. travel
C. (Individual writing)
D. 1. had not hit
   2. had been ; would have been
   3. would have survived ; had been
   4. would have stopped ; had warned
   5. had been ; would not have occurred
   6. had kept ; would not have been punished
   7. would have won ; had not missed
   8. had been locked ; would not have run
E. 1. ✔
   2. I would be a multi-millionaire if I won the lottery.
   3. If he had tried just a little harder, he would have passed the test.
   4. They would not have succeeded if you had not helped them.
   5. We would have waited for him if he had called.
   6. ✔
   7. ✔
   8. The outcome would have been totally different if he hadn't made the wrong decision.
   9. Don't reveal it even if they ask you.
   10. ✔
   11. ✔

16 Conditional Clauses (2)

A. (Individual writing)
B. 1. Had they told me about it, I would not have made such a remark.
   2. Were I elected president, I would make you the treasurer.
   3. They wouldn't have made the trip had they read the news.
   4. Had he teamed up with me, we would have won the tournament.
   5. Should they appear, I would sneak out by the backdoor.
   6. They would be held responsible were they at the scene.
   7. They couldn't have beaten us had we stayed focused.
   8. Had the teacher announced it in advance, there wouldn't have been so much anxiety.
C. (Suggested answers)
   1. unless 2. Even if
   3. as long as / so long as 4. As long as / So long as
   5. unless 6. even if
   7. only if
   8. as long as / so long as / provided that
   9. unless
   10. Unless
D. 1. Unless they remain quiet for the rest of the lesson, the teacher will make them stay behind.
   2. ✔
   3. As long as you don't say a word, I will leave the matter behind.
   4. They will go ahead unless you tell them not to.
   5. The show will be held as planned, provided that the venue is confirmed.
   6. Had he not been careful, he would have fallen into the water and drowned.
   7. ✔

8. Even if you had signed the document, they wouldn't have approved the funding.
9. ✔
10. If your mother had discovered it, you would have been in trouble.

Review 2

A. noun ; neither ; neither ; noun ; neither ; appositive ; appositive ; noun
B. (Individual writing of sentences)
   1. indicative 2. subjunctive 3. imperative
   4. subjunctive 5. indicative 6. subjunctive
   7. indicative
C. 1. An Egyptian dance was performed by the girls in Act One.
   2. The procession of animals was led across the stage by Michael.
   3. The never-ending Act Two was wrapped up by the majestic march.
   4. A hole was accidentally made in Andrea's bulky costume.
   5. Lola's shoulder was sniffed by the elephant when it came near.
   6. Everything we do should be treated as though it were a dress rehearsal.
   7. The Egyptian dance and the excellent singing were appreciated by the audience.
   8. The curtain was raised again by the stagehand for the cast to take a final bow.
D. 1. To make it look seamless, every detail needed rehearsing.
   2. Some soloists needed reassuring to perform their best.
   3. The costumes needed cleaning after each production.
E. 1. interrogative 2. conditional 3. compound
   4. declarative 5. exclamatory 6. imperative
F. 1. noun 2. noun 3. adjective
   4. adverb 5. noun 6. adjective
   7. adverb
G. 1. ✔
   2. ✘ ; If you need more paper, just tell me.
   3. ✔
   4. ✘ ; I would not have lost my turtle if I had kept an eye on it.
   5. ✘ ; This picture would be more colourful if I were the one painting it.
   6. ✔
   7. ✔
H. (Suggested writing)
   Dave asked Shelley if she had known about a special exhibit at the National Gallery of Canada in Ottawa. Shelley did not know about it, so Dave told her that the exhibit was called "Wilderness in the City", showing the works of Emily Carr. Excited, Shelley told Dave that Emily Carr was her favourite Canadian artist. It turned out that she was Dave's favourite as well. He loved Emily Carr's spiritual paintings of the forests in British Columbia. Shelley thought that she made the wilderness look very mysterious. Dave added that it looked romantic too. The exhibit ran from March 3 to May 10, and the two of them would go on Saturday.

ISBN: 978-1-897164-42-6

1 Choice of Words

A. (Individual answers)
B. (Individual answers)
C. (Individual writing)

2 Adding Emphasis

A. 1. Almost all the villagers were killed by the flood.
   2. The ringleader was caught by the police during the raid.
   3. The raging fire was finally put out by the firefighters after more than five hours.
   4. The sculpture was removed from the square by someone in the heat of the night.
   5. The players on the bench were told by the coach to step up their effort if they wanted to play more regularly.
B. (Suggested writing)
   1. Seldom have I felt so helpless.
   2. Hardly had the police arrived at the scene when the car exploded.
   3. Little did he realize the magnitude of the problem.
   4. Never did we expect to be able to sweep the champion team.
   5. Little did she know that it was no longer a secret.
   6. Rarely did they dine at the restaurants in the neighbourhood.
   7. Little does Keith know that he has been set up.
   8. Never have I seen a lobster this big!
C. 1. We did go to the haunted house on Halloween.
   2. She does know how to solve the problem.
   3. Fred did apologize to Helen for embarrassing her.
   4. The raccoon did build a home in my garage.
   5. I do believe that we still stand a chance in the game.
   6. The driver did stop to make sure he didn't hit anyone.
   7. The magician does perform for us every Saturday evening.
   8. The principal did ask me to help her out with the filing work.
   9. We do swim twice a week to keep fit.
D. 1. What he wanted was a room all to himself.
   2. It was Mary who was elected captain, not Melissa.
   3. It was her brother who ate half of the fruitcake. / What her brother ate was half of the fruitcake.
   4. It was they who tried to make everyone happy. / What they tried was to make everyone happy.
   5. It was I who revealed the truth to the principal. / What I revealed to the principal was the truth.
   6. It was Heather who had mistakenly taken the windbreaker home. / What Heather had mistakenly taken home was the windbreaker.
   7. What he must do is keep his chin up and start all over again.

3 Words that Help Build Paragraphs

A. (Individual writing)
B. (Individual writing)
C. (Individual writing)
D. (Individual writing)

4 Paragraphs

A. (Individual writing)
B. (Individual writing)
C. (Individual writing)
D. (Individual writing)

5 Clustering Ideas

A. (Individual writing)
B. (Individual writing)
C. (Individual writing)
D. (Individual writing)

6 Organization

A. (Individual writing)
B. (Individual writing)
C. (Individual writing)
D. (Individual writing)

7 Clarity in Writing

A. The first paragraph is easier to follow, because it moves from the past ("When I was young...") to the present ("Now, the lake has changed a lot."), whereas the second paragraph jumps from the past to the present and back to the past again.
B. 1. Canada geese spend their summer in northern regions. In the fall, they start migrating to warmer regions as far south as Mexico. Canada geese migrate in flocks that vary in size. Smaller geese tend to migrate in larger flocks than larger geese do, and season flocks tend to be made up of more geese than early season flocks.
   2. New Brunswick is one of Canada's three Maritime provinces. It is the only officially bilingual province in the country. There are approximately 750 000 people living in New Brunswick. The majority of them are English-speaking. The French-speaking minority constitute about 35% of the population. As a bilingual province, New Brunswick has a comprehensive parallel Anglophone and Francophone public school system from kindergarten to grade 12.
C. 1. People will pay attention to you if you speak with confidence and carry yourself properly.
   2. Few people were interested since there was insufficient publicity and the cast was weak.
   3. They will listen to you if you can provide evidence to prove that you were not there.
   4. The guests expected spicy dishes and exotic drinks.
D. (Suggested writing)
   1. Until we can get more details, we don't know whether or not we should proceed as planned.

ISBN: 978-1-897164-42-6

2. If you listen carefully to how the beginning is played, the music sounds like a piece composed by David Foster.
3. Although you may not know, everyone is ready to pitch in, including Mr. and Mrs. Schuler.

E. (Suggested writing)
1. We met to discuss two main issues: endorse the plan and amend the rules.
2. The committee is now considering the proposal.
3. When we arrived in Paris, we decided to visit the Eiffel Tower first.

8 Narrative Writing (1)

A. 1. On Friday afternoon, I was riding home from school on a bus. It was very crowded, as everyone seemed to be hurrying home for the long weekend. I was standing in the middle of the bus next to a young lad in a red T-shirt. An old woman was sitting opposite us. She was dozing off, holding onto her handbag.
2. It was a chilly night. The boys hurriedly put on their Halloween costumes while chattering away with delight in anticipation of one of their favourite days. They couldn't wait for the festivities of the evening to begin. Tonight they would trick-or-treat to their hearts' content, raking in the goodies. Then they would all go back to Ken's home. His mom and dad would inspect their goodies before they could eat them.

B. (Individual writing)
C. (Individual writing)
D. (Individual writing)

9 Narrative Writing (2)

A. When Helen Keller was 19 months old, she fell ill. ~~Babies get sick easily, and like other parents, Helen's parents weren't too concerned about it at the beginning. They left Helen with the maid.~~ Days passed but Helen didn't seem to get any better. Helen's parents started to worry and they took her to the doctor's. The doctor thought that it was "brain fever" that Helen was suffering from. In those days, brain fever was a deadly disease. ~~To this day the nature of her ailment remains a mystery. Modern day doctors think it may have been scarlet fever or meningitis.~~ Helen was, for many days, expected to die. Eventually, the fever subsided, and Helen's parents were relieved, believing that their daughter was well again.

However, Helen's mother soon noticed how her daughter was failing to respond when the dinner bell was rung or when she passed her hand in front of her daughter's eyes. It was evident that Helen's illness had left her both deaf and blind. ~~What a tragedy for Helen! Imagine a child who can't hear or see for the rest of her life!~~

B. (Individual writing)
C. (Individual writing)
D. (Individual writing)

10 Writing Reviews (1)

A. A. background information
   B. category
   C. background information
   D. description
   E. evaluation

B. (Individual writing)

C. Movie:
   Positive:
   stunning effects ; amusing dialogues ; elaborate costumes ; exciting opening ; inspiring theme
   Negative:
   slow tempo ; fragmented plot ; unimaginable script ; predictable storyline ; disappointing ending
   Restaurant:
   Positive:
   ample portions ; relaxed atmosphere ; award-winning dishes
   Negative:
   bland taste ; slow service ; aloof attitude ; uncomfortable seats ; noisy atmosphere

D. The Little Sicily is located in Fairview Centre Mall, 237 Fairview Blvd., Incline Village. It has been an Incline Village favourite for more than 20 years.

Family owned and operated, the service is friendly and the cozy restaurant feels as if you were at your friend's dining room, though the brown lacquer panels on the white walls look somewhat dull.

The Little Sicily serves a dozen pasta dishes and many pizzas, as well as chicken, veal, shrimp, and beef. Dinners include soup or salad, a vegetable, and olive-oil garlic bread. I tried their Seafood Portofino Special: a huge dish of assorted shellfish in a delicious red sauce – it was simply delicious!

And don't forget to try their homemade tiramisu, which is the best I've ever had! Prices are somewhat on the high side, though, but the quality is worth it.

I'd give it a rating of 4.8 out of 5! A must-try restaurant.

11 Writing Reviews (2)

A. Stronger:
   totally ; very ; especially ; extremely ; really ; particularly
   Weaker:
   slightly ; rather ; quite ; fairly ; somewhat ; reasonably

B. (Suggested answers)
   1. hugely
   2. very
   3. delightfully
   4. really
   5. unbelievably
   6. pretty
   7. somewhat
   8. rather
   9. quite
   10. fairly
   11. extremely
   12. very

C. (Individual writing)

ISBN: 978-1-897164-42-6

D. (Suggested writing)
1. He was excited to have been able to catch a rather huge bass.
2. That was reasonably good French cuisine.
3. The slow tempo of the show made it extremely boring.
4. Everyone especially enjoyed Kate's performance.
E. (Individual writing)

12 Argumentative Writing

A. (Individual writing)
B. (Individual writing)
C. (Individual writing)

13 The Editing Process (1)

A. Before the adoption of the written Hindu-Arabic numeral
system, the abacus was <u>allready</u> used widely as a
[already]

calculation <u>toll</u>. In fact; it is still used by some merchants
[tool] [,]

and clerks in China and Japan.

The typical abacus is about 20 cm tall and it comes in various
widths <u>depanding</u> on the application. It usually has more
[depending]

than seven rods; there are two beads on each rod in the

upper deck and five beads each in the bottom. The beads

are counted by moving them up or down towards the

beam - Many Chinese and Japanese can use the abacus
at high speed, based on a set of <u>techniues</u>, to do
[techniques]
<u>multipication</u>, division, addition, subtraction, and even
[multiplication]

square root and cubic root operations.

B. 1. Neither Jenny nor Danielle is held responsible for the accident.
2. Here is a list of things that I need to complete before school ends.
3. The only option left was to call the company and ask for the spare part to be shipped as soon as possible.
4. Greg doesn't seem to realize the gravity of the problem and keeps the matter to himself.
5. Each of them wants a share of the fruitcake but there just isn't enough for all of them.
C. (Suggested writing)
1. The hike took us five hours to complete. It was tiring but interesting. We also saw quite a few rare species of insects.
2. The show was supposed to start at eight. Somehow it was delayed but no one knew why, so the audience became disgruntled.
3. The project took longer than we had expected. Although we had to burn the midnight oil for the whole week, we were unable to meet the deadline. Luckily, Mrs. Davis agreed to let us work on it for two more days.
4. The crowd gathered in front of the town hall. They demanded to meet with the mayor but the clerk came out and told them that the mayor was not in. They had to disperse or he would call the police.
5. The left fielder misread the ball and was too late to dive for it. The ball just bounced to the far corner. The left fielder quickly picked himself up and ran to get it but by then, the opposing team had already scored two runs.
D. Many of us must have used an abacus-like counting tool when we were in kindergarten or grade school. In fact, this form of "abacus" is being used around the world as an aid in teaching the numeral system to small children. Each bead on this abacus has the same value. It can represent numbers up to 100. A significant educational advantage of using this counting tool is that it gives the child an awareness of the groupings of ten which are the foundation of the numeral system.

14 The Editing Process (2)

A. Group 1:
Have you ever wondered why a puck, and not a ball, is used in ice hockey? When hockey was first introduced to North America from Europe, players did use a rubber ball, much like what was used in field hockey. However, they soon found that the rubber ball used in field hockey was far too active on the hard ice surface. They came up with an idea – cut off the top and bottom of the ball to form the hockey puck! Wasn't that an ingenius idea?
Group 2:
During a hockey game, the puck can reach a speed of more than 160 kilometres an hour. It is extremely dangerous to players and spectators when they are struck by it. In fact, puck-related injuries at hockey games are not uncommon. The most serious incident involving a spectator took place on March 18, 2002. A 13-year-old girl died two days after being struck on the head by a hockey puck deflected into the crowd at a National Hockey League game. As a result of this tragedy, glass panels sitting atop the boards of hockey rinks have been supplemented with mesh nets that extend above the upper edge of the glass.
B. 1. In ice hockey, the puck is used instead of a ball. A puck is a hard, black disk made of rubber. A standard puck, which is made of rubber, is 25.4 mm thick, 76.2 mm in diameter, and weighs between 156 and 170 g in weight. Pucks are often marked with a team or league logo on one or both faces. We can find team or league logos on hockey pucks.
2. An American TV network once developed a "smart" puck. The "smart" puck had integrated electronics to track its position on screen. The electronics inside the puck was able to show the track clearly on screen. A blue streak traced the path of the "smart" puck across the ice. The streak would turn red if the "smart" puck was shot especially hard. This was an experiment to help viewers better follow the game by making the puck more visible. With the streak, the puck was more visible on screen.

ISBN: 978-1-897164-42-6

3. The "smart" puck was first put to use in 1996, but traditional hockey fans did not like the idea. They thought that it spoiled the original form of the hockey game. And the "smart" puck did not meet its intended objective of drawing new viewers to the game either. ~~Hockey fans did not like the "smart" puck and the "smart" puck was unable to draw more viewers.~~ As a result, the experiment was stopped in 1998. ~~The TV network discontinued using the "smart" puck.~~

C. (Suggested writing)
   1. The trophy became known as the Stanley Cup.
   2. The players control the puck using a hockey stick, which is a long stick with a blade that is commonly curved at one end.
   3. In women's ice hockey, bodychecking is not allowed.

ISBN: 978-1-897164-42-6

ISBN: 978-1-897164-42-6